Economic Crises in World Agriculture

Economic Crises
in
World Agriculture

by
Theodore W. Schultz

Ann Arbor
The University of Michigan Press

Preface

There is a juncture in economic development when
a stagnant and depressed agriculture causes a crisis.
Country after country has reached this juncture.
They are countries that have concentrated on the expansion of industrial production, but a monolithic
pursuit of industrialization is not enough to attain
an optimum rate of growth. For want of economic
opportunities, farmers do not save and invest to increase agricultural production. For want of progress
in agriculture, industrialization is in jeopardy. Then
comes the crisis. In the Argentine it came during the
Perón regime. The industrialization of China ground
to a halt in the late fifties. Nor has the Soviet Union
been spared. The crisis in India brings back famine
fears. While not so dramatic, many of the less-developed countries are at this juncture. Although be-
latedly, inescapably they all must face the issue:
"What is to be done about agriculture?"

My first three chapters are devoted to this issue.
The first two are based on the analytical approach
set forth in my *Transforming Traditional Agriculture*
(Yale University Press, 1964). In the third chapter I
consider the implications of this approach for our
many efforts abroad to assist other countries in
modernizing their agriculture and examine the programs of our leading private foundations, the
programs of our land-grant universities abroad, and
those of U.S.-AID missions. This chapter draws
mainly on a paper I prepared for the American As-

sociation for the Advancement of Science.

In the final chapter I turn to modern agriculture with special reference to the United States. Here we are at a juncture which has given rise to a wholly different type of economic crisis. An approach to an understanding of what has happened is presented, and the policy implications that emerge from this approach are examined.

The chapters of this book were given as the William W. Cook Lectures on American Institutions at The University of Michigan. Allan F. Smith, dean of the University of Michigan Law School, was my host who anticipated my every want. My secretary, Mrs. Virginia Thurner, competently and with exacting care saw to it that my manuscript was in order, corrected the proof, and saw that the index was properly prepared.

Theodore W. Schultz

The University of Chicago
September 1964

Contents

I: AN ECONOMIC APPROACH   1

A World Picture
Perverse Farmers
Surpluses and Shortages
Damages to Trade
Production Puzzles
Economic Basis
Clues
Income Elasticity
Land and Capital
Farm Size
Real and Relevant Basis
Hypotheses Concerning Traditional Agriculture

II: TRADITIONAL AGRICULTURE   18

Preferences
Selling Economics Short
Grist for Economics
The Two Myths
A Bad Press
Production Possibilities
Supply Response
The Allocative Test
Profitability of Investment
Necessary Conclusions

III: ECONOMIC GROWTH FROM
TRADITIONAL AGRICULTURE   41

Economic Basis Again
Private Profit Incentives Not Sufficient
The Lack of Success and Reasons for It
An Efficient Approach

viii   *Economic Crises in World Agriculture*

IV: MODERN AGRICULTURE   69

Productivity
Soviet Plight
Losses in Farm Income from Productivity Growth
Why Welfare Services for Farm People Are
   Neglected
   Influence of the Southern Tradition
   Conflicts of Interest
   A Lack of Knowledge
   Price-Production Programs

Notes   97
Index   111

I

An Economic Approach

Economists and poets have long cherished the virtues of farmers. Unlike the organization men, farmers are free, independent, and above all self-reliant. Frugality and work are part of their yeomen heritage. So it is easy to understand agriculture and farm life. Thus oriented, the economist sees agriculture as a simple type of production, not complicated by sticky prices, barriers to entry, and excess capacity. Competition is assured, for there are always many farmers. How convenient in teaching economic principles that the economic behavior of farmers always supported one's blackboard diagrams! But all this is now past; the idyllic picture of farm life has been replaced, and we do not understand the new picture, which seems strange, baffling, and full of unresolved puzzles. Wherever we look the economic behavior of farmers confounds us.

Perverse Farmers

Farmers have seemingly become perverse everywhere. In China, where they were given the command to take a big leap forward, they promptly stepped backward. In Russia they were ordered to grow corn in old settled areas and wheat on new land; and now Russia has neither enough corn nor wheat. In India despite the large planned investment in agriculture, and the many efforts of our U.S.-AID mission, assisted by a number of our land-grant colleges and the pioneering agricultural programs of our largest private foundations, agricultural production has not done well—actually declining somewhat in recent years. Meanwhile, in Western Europe, West Germany proudly proclaims an open competitive economy, but her farmers have insisted on and have been given an exceedingly high level of protection. Nor has the United States been spared, for we have enacted all manner of legislation backed by billions of dollars of appropriations to induce farmers to reduce production, but farmers have kept on increasing it, attaining a new record high in 1963.

Surpluses and Shortages

From another point of view we see both surpluses and shortages. Large burdensome stocks of farm products have accumulated, notably in the United States, while there is far from enough food in most of the populous countries of Asia. No matter how perfect international commodity markets are at matching demand and supply, they cannot solve this problem of food deficits. Nor are international commodity arrangements able to resolve it. If there were any doubts on this issue one need only examine the distributional effects of the international wheat agreement and such doubts would be dispelled. Nor has our gigantic Public Law 480 program of transferring billions of dollars of our farm surpluses to poor countries made an appreciable dent in resolving the problem of not enough food in these poor countries. Meanwhile, we have reasons to be worried about the adverse side effects of this program upon farm product prices and agricultural production within the recipient countries. In India it may well be that Indian farmers have been receiving less for the rice and wheat they have been producing than they would have received had there not been large imports of United States' farm products made available under the P.L. 480 programs. But can India afford this kind of underpricing and thus discourage her domestic production of farm products? Once this issue is seen clearly the answer will be no.[1]

Damages to Trade

Nor is this all of the international trade picture. Some of the less-developed countries are sorely dependent on selling farm products abroad in order to acquire the foreign exchange needed to buy capital goods and to hire skilled personnel from abroad to help them modernize. But we are making it increasingly hard for poor countries to promote their economic growth by this means. While we feature our economic aid to assist them in their economic development, at the same time we pursue an agricultural policy that thwarts their efforts to achieve more economic growth. To make matters even worse for such underdeveloped countries, Western Europeans are in general doing the same as we are doing.

The subsidization of agricultural production in the United States and in Western Europe has gone so far that there are now some who interpret the consequences as evidence that the comparative advantage of these highly industrialized countries is no longer in industrial but in agricultural production. By this strange twist of the evidence, the underdeveloped countries will find it to their advantage not only to reduce their exports of farm products, where they still are exporting, but even to import an increasing part of their food requirements, presumably paying for them by exporting industrial goods to Western Europe and the United States! Little wonder that such specious reasoning should lead to confusion and bafflement.

Production Puzzles

Thus we see the apparent perversity of farmers, the perverted subsidization of farm production in the affluent countries, and the adverse side effects of food aid upon the recipient countries, under the long shadow of surpluses and unrequited deficits. What we do not see are the underlying puzzles in agricultural production.[2] I only mention them here, for I shall come back to them.

1. The agricultural success of Japan, despite formidable limitations in land and the fact that the advance in knowledge applicable to Western agriculture is not readily useful in Japanese farming, is as yet not explained. Although Japan in per capita terms has only one-sixth as much agricultural land as India and although her farms are mere postage

stamps, agricultural production between the prewar years and 1962 rose 90 percent.[3] In rice, unbelievably, Japan is on the verge of becoming an exporter.

2. Except for Japan and for Taiwan the populous countries of Asia appear to face unfavorable returns in applying capital and labor to land. Why should unfavorable returns be so enthroned in these countries?

3. Our approach, which consists of nonprofit research, of extension work and schooling for farm people, and of a vast number of private firms operating for profit, has been unbelievably successful in terms of production. Yet in our efforts abroad to assist poor countries to develop a modern agriculture, our approach has been far from successful, as, for example, in our record in India. Why this lack of success abroad?

4. While it is easy to belittle the performance of agriculture in the Soviet Union, it is not obvious why it has performed so badly. Research has long been highly valued in Russia. Nor did the government make the mistake of atomizing the agricultural research establishment by placing it piecemeal under state and collective farms. There also has been a strong commitment to modernize agriculture, symbolized by the tractor and hybrid corn. Why then has the payoff not been larger?

5. Lastly, there is the puzzle implicit in the large divergency between inputs and outputs that has characterized agriculture in the United States. From 1940 to 1960, for example, total farm output increased fully 50 percent, whereas our official meas-

ures of total agricultural inputs increased about 5 percent. This implies ten units of additional output for each unit of additional input. Is it possible to have "favorable returns" over time on so grand a scale? How can one explain it?

Obviously, this picture of agriculture is far different from the one poets and economists once eulogized. The new perplexities have attracted the attention of students of politics, culture, and law. Lawyers, for instance, have examined the legal basis of agricultural credit and farm tenure in some of the less-developed countries. Anthropologists have done much to deepen our knowledge of folk societies. Students of government have provided an essential dimension by examining the political process of land reform and of governmental planning. But for all that, the economic aspects of this picture are important, and an understanding of them is necessary in determining the optimum contribution that agriculture can make to economic growth.

Since it is not difficult to show that farmers are not perverse economic men, it will be unnecessary to await the findings of a royal commission to discover that the particular perversities we behold are simple economic responses to specific public and private actions, the consequences of which should have been anticipated. It requires only a small chain of economic logic, which is well anchored empirically, to demonstrate that the subsidization of agricultural production impairs not only the economic efficiency of the agricultural sector but also reduces the gains to be had from international trade. There is a remedy for the unwanted side effects of Public Law 480 aid to poor countries. The large deficiencies of food in parts of Asia and elsewhere are unfortunately beyond our capacity to remedy by means of more "free" food. Even if we were to double our production and make all the additional output available, we could not distribute so large a surplus of food in poor countries without critically undermining the incentives for growth on the part of the principal economic sector of these countries.

The fact is that these food shortages cannot be permanently satisfied except by large increases in agricultural production within these countries and by a marked decline in population growth. Vast quantities of "free" food from abroad can at best only serve particular transitory objectives. Instead of strengthening the incentives to increase the permanent capacity of agriculture abroad, they weaken these incentives. Nor are they a means for altering the basic values of people in relation to population growth. For that matter, cheaper food from internal production also is not sufficient to alter these values, for it is patently clear that in many poor countries, population growth is negating most of the potential gains in per capita food consumption that could be had from their own increases in agricultural production.

These issues can be taken in stride. But not so the production puzzles, for they confront us with major unsettled economic questions. To clarify these questions it will be necessary to simplify the otherwise all too complex picture of world agriculture.

I shall consider two simple models, one to explain agricultural production where farmers are under the economic restraints of the traditional agriculture characteristic of farming in many poor countries, and the other to explain agricultural production as presently observed in an array of countries, including the United States, Canada, Australia, New Zealand, most of the countries of Western Europe, Japan, Israel, and Mexico. The two models represent the two agricultures of the world to be discussed. They permit me to draw inferences with respect to the possibilities for economic growth from each of these two types of agriculture.

Before presenting a proposal—along with the economic basis on which it rests—for an efficient approach to modernizing traditional agriculture, I shall examine in some detail the sources of economic growth from traditional agriculture. Thus, I leave until last, the economic efficiency and welfare issues that confront us in adjusting modern agriculture, the objectives of which are to bring demand and supply into a workable balance.

ECONOMIC BASIS

We can rank agriculture throughout the world in accordance with the contribution it is making to economic growth. For this purpose economic growth means simply increases in national income. Agriculture is then one of the sources of national income. A classification of countries based on this criterion gives a wide array of differences. In many countries agriculture contributes little to economic growth, but in some countries it contributes much. I propose to concentrate on these two end sets and treat each of them as a distinct economic type. I refer to the one as *traditional* agriculture, and to the other, for want of a better term, as *modern* agriculture.

This approach implies forbearance with respect to the simplification and requires that each set be thought of as an idealized economic type in relation to economic growth. To do this it will be essential not to think in terms of growing rice or wheat, small or large farms, subsistence or commercial farms, farmland that is poor or highly productive, and differences in the cultural characteristics of farm people. Instead, one must think of those attributes of agriculture and the economy in which it is situated that determine how little one set and how much the other contributes to economic growth. Let us thus try to discover the economic attributes which are the key to economic growth from agriculture.

Clues

We may begin by looking at agriculture in India as if it were predominantly of the traditional type and that of the United States as of the modern type. People in India are, of course, very poor and can afford only a meager diet of slightly over 2000 calories a day per person, two-thirds of which consists of grain products, whereas in the United States this average is well over 3000 calories daily, only a fifth of which consists of grain products.[4]

One clue might be the marked difference in *the pro-*

portion of the personal income that is spent on food:
in India about three-fifths and in the United States
one-fifth of the income of consumers goes for food.[5]
But this difference, following Engel's law, is a consequence of the very low and the high real per capita
income of consumers in the two countries. Although
it is often said—even by some economists—that the
small share of consumers' expenditures for food is
one of the blessings of our agriculture, it is far from
true, because the high level of income in the United
States is only to a small extent due to the productivity
of American farms. This has been cogently put by
Houthakker in his sharp criticism of Wilcox's convenient views on this issue.[6] Thus, this is a false lead.

Income Elasticity

Closely akin is the apparently sophisticated view
based on the concept of demand, where the appeal is
to the differences in the income elasticity of the
demand for food. It is still high in India, which means
that with an increase in consumer income, other
things unchanged, substantially more food would be
consumed, whereas in the United States the income
elasticity of the demand for the farm-produced components of food is very low.[7] While these differences
are exceedingly important in understanding why the
demand for farm-produced foods, even though the
rate of population growth were the same, will increase
much more in poor countries as real per capita income
rises than it will in the affluent countries, it too is
a false clue. And the reason is the same as before: that
is, the observed income elasticities depend primarily

on the level of consumer income, which in turn depends on the flow of income from all sectors of an economy, among which agriculture may have become minor, as is obviously the case in the United States.

Land and Capital

Is the availability and use of additional farmland to grow crops the key to this puzzle? Surely not during the last two decades; for in India which has done badly in agriculture the gross area sown to crops seems to have increased substantially, whereas in the United States the cropland harvested in 1962 was over one-sixth below the peak reached in the early 1940's.[8]

Is it the formation of additional capital in farming? Here too the answer is no, provided the form of the additional capital is as of old, although data are far from satisfactory. In the United States the stock of capital represented by livestock and machinery—including motor vehicles on farms—increased about two-fifths between 1940 and 1962.[9] Meanwhile, in India the stock of durable material capital in agriculture—excluding land and houses—seems to have increased at about the same rate.[10] The critical difference in this connection is not so much in the rates at which the stock of reproducible farm capital has risen but, as I shall show, in the types of capital that are formed and in the rates of return to investment in agriculture.

Farm Size

There is also the appeal that is always made to the size of farms—based on the presumption that modern agriculture requires large farms, for how else can the tractor be used? Of course, countries with a large population relative to farmland are understandably confronted by strong population pressure against land. Much of Asia faces this pressure. The nine Asian countries listed in Table 1 have farms

Table 1

Farm Size, Production per Acre, and Production per Capita of the Rural Sector of Nine Asian Countries

	Average size of farms[1]	Production per acre[2]	Agricultural production per capita of rural sector[3]
	A C R E S	D O L L A R S	D O L L A R S
Thailand	9.5	42	45
Philippines	8.8	74	72
Burma	7.6	49	79
Cambodia	5.6	48	47
India	5.4	33	39
Pakistan	4.2	55	54
Indonesia	3.3	60	38
Taiwan	3.1	279	114
Japan	2.1	274	102

SOURCE: Lester R. Brown, *An Economic Analysis of Far Eastern Agriculture.* Foreign Agric. Econ. Report No. 2, U.S.D.A. (November 1961).

[1] From Table 6, p. 11, in terms of permanently cultivatable land excluding wasteland and grazing land.

[2] From Table 16, p. 25, based on annual production per acre of agricultural land for 1957-59, valued at 1958 world market prices.

[3] From Table 17, p. 26, based on annual agricultural production for 1957-59, valued at 1958 world market prices, and the rural population.

that average from 9.5 acres in Thailand to 2.1 acres in Japan.[11] That difference in the size of farms may not be a clue here is strongly indicated when one compares India and Japan. Although farms in India are fully two and a half times as large as they are in Japan—5.4 and 2.1 acres respectively—Japanese agriculture is substantially modern (even in terms of tractors—over a million[12]), while that in India is still largely of the traditional type.

In looking for clues there are also some recent doctrinal views that get nowhere because they are demonstrably false. Disguised unemployment in agriculture in poor countries is one of them. Another is based on the belief that farmers either do not respond to changes in product and factor prices, or, if they do, they respond perversely. I referred to this issue briefly at the outset and shall present strong evidence in Chapter II which contradicts this baneful doctrine. Still another in effect seriously maligns farmers in poor countries by alleging that they lack particular economic virtues. What is frequently said is that they are not thrifty and not industrious, and that they lack entrepreneurship. But I shall show shortly that these are in general false allegations.

Real and Relevant Basis

Traditional agriculture consists of farming under a long-established economic equilibrium, which is attained during generations of farming, and the critical conditions on which it depends have remained virtually constant for generations. In sharp contrast, modern agriculture is in general in a state of disequilibrium—a chronic moving economic disequilibrium. Here the critical conditions have been changing continuously during recent decades, so that farmers, despite their adjustments, appear to be on an economic treadmill. They have not arrived at a stable economic equilibrium; instead it keeps on eluding them.

My approach, then, is to apply the concept of a long-established economic equilibrium in determining the production possibilities of traditional agriculture. It will prove to be a powerful engine for analysis. For modern agriculture, it will be more useful to apply a set of disequilibrium concepts.

But clearly this approach confronts one with the paradox that farmers in traditional agriculture do better than those in modern agriculture in exhausting the economic opportunities open to them. Theoretically, when a sector of an economy is at the idealized equilibrium, it is producing at an optimum. Suppose then that traditional agriculture has long since arrived at such an equilibrium, the implication is that it is producing precisely the right products in the right amounts and that it is using the agricultural factors of production in the right proportion and amounts, and therefore it is contributing a maximum to the national product. More than that it cannot do. This would then be a bleak picture for economic growth from traditional agriculture. Contrariwise, when a sector of an economy is in disequilibrium, it means that the real production possibilities are not being fully exploited. Thus, national income can be increased, and such is the situation with respect to modern agriculture. The irony here is that traditional agriculture which produces so little cannot produce more as things now stand and that modern agriculture which produces so abundantly can render even more to economic growth than it is already contributing.

This conception of two agricultures, while favorable to the modern type in terms of economic growth, provides little comfort for those who believe that improvements in the economic efficiency of traditional agriculture will result in a large payoff. The economist thus faces an analytical choice which he dislikes intensely. While the problem in the case of modern agriculture can be resolved by means of "better resource allocation," the problem that he must face in coping with traditional agriculture requires a search for ways of breaking the established economic equilibrium and creating a disequilibrium which calls for an approach which is an anathema to most economists. But the fact of the matter is that programs, the aim of which is to modernize traditional agriculture, must break the long-standing economic equilibrium that characterizes farming in so many poor countries. My plan is to examine with care how this can be accomplished.

HYPOTHESES CONCERNING
TRADITIONAL AGRICULTURE

It will be convenient to present here—in a preliminary fashion—some of the more important deductions that are implicit in my approach. Since these deductions are based on particular premises and are derived by economic logic, they should be viewed as economic hypotheses. It turns out that they are testable, and such empirical evidence as is now available supports them.

In order to avoid some complications, let me postpone the particular deductions that can be drawn with respect to modern agriculture. For traditional agriculture, the following hypotheses will serve to guide the analysis.

Given the land at the disposal of farmers and the state of their knowledge, *they are not underutilizing the land* by the way they farm. *Nor are they misallocating the reproducible material capital at their disposal*—their draft animals, implements, wells and ditches for irrigation, and other useful structures. It may come as a surprise to find that the stock of such capital is often very large in traditional agriculture, especially where it depends upon irrigation.

Given the land and the forms of material capital available to farmers and the state of their knowledge, *they are not misallocating their own labor nor other labor that is available to them.* The widely held notion that traditional agriculture is honeycombed with all manner of underemployment is not compatible with this hypothesis. Underemployment in a strict economic sense is consistent with the types of disequilibria that characterize modern agriculture but not with the equilibrium of traditional agriculture. More important, however, in this connection is the doctrine which holds that there is much labor of zero value in traditional agriculture. As it is viewed here, the doctrine of agricultural labor of zero value pertains only to those persons who want to work, who are capable of working, and who are in fact working. This doctrine is not consistent with the hypothesis here advanced.[13]

But the most telling hypothesis with respect to economic growth over a period of time is that *the rate of return to investment in order to increase production in traditional agriculture is very low,* so low that there is little or no incentive to acquire credit or to increase savings for this purpose.

II

Traditional Agriculture

The prayer "Give us this day our daily bread,"[1] voices man's ancient fear of starvation. Anxiety with regard to food from an uncertain nature is an age-old concern[2]:

> *It is in vain that you rise early*
> *to go late to rest,*
> *eating the bread of anxious toil.*

and

> *He gave their crops to the caterpillar*
> *and the fruit of their labor to the locust.*
> *He destroyed their vines with hail,*
> *and their sycamores with frost.*

For us these are empty psalms. We take our food for granted. Our anxiety is nuclear destruction. But for many of the world's people it is still the ancient fear of not having enough food. They are still bound to a niggardly and often precarious agriculture.

Why is traditional agriculture so niggardly? As I have already suggested, the meager increase in output of traditional agriculture is not a consequence of indolence or because of a lack of thrift. It is not because of some quirk in people's preferences as I shall show shortly. Instead, it is a matter of costs and

18

returns. The marginal returns to labor, to land, and to reproducible material capital are very low. Stated another way, the *price of increasing the capacity* of traditional agriculture, as things stand, is high. Statistics are sometimes superfluous. There can be no doubt that the price is very high when one sees Indians growing potatoes on the highlands of Peru, or farmers cropping the hillsides of Haiti, or slashing trees in the Brazilian tropics to clear a field, or planting a paddy of rice in India. But it has been so for ages. The archeological records of the Sumerian, Babylonian, Egyptian, and Greek civilizations all indicate that they, too, found the sources of food costly to develop and dear to hold against intruders.

The picture of world agriculture with which I began will serve as a preface here. Farmers are not perverse economic men in responding to economic incentives, whether one observes them in China, the Soviet Union, India, Japan, or the United States. The designs of policy in most European countries and the United States are reducing the gains to be had from international trade in farm products and they are imposing a burden upon those poor countries which must export farm products to acquire capital goods and some skills from abroad to modernize their economies. It is impossible by means of economic aid alone to supply the additional food that many a poor country would need to attain an adequate diet. The quantity and quality of food required for such a diet can only be attained ultimately by increasing agricultural production in these countries and by using it for this purpose rather than for population growth.

While considering agricultural production I directed attention to important production puzzles, that is, to the unexplained success of Japan, the poor record of India despite plans and aid, the lack of success from tractors, hybrid corn, and other inputs to modernize agriculture in the Soviet Union, and in marked contrast, the continuing increases in agricultural production in the United States with virtually no increases in total agricultural inputs, as conventionally measured, and notwithstanding all manner of federal programs to curtail output. These puzzles lead me to the concept of economic growth based on the price of income streams. A classification of agriculture based on this concept reveals a wide array of differences among countries. Modern agriculture is at one end of such an array, where this price is relatively low, and at the other end are many communities where farming is under the restraints of traditional agriculture, which make economic growth so expensive that people can ill afford it.

According to my preliminary sketch, traditional agriculture has the earmarks of long-established economic equilibrium with respect to savings, investment, and production. With this sketch as a premise several testable hypotheses are derived. One set indicates that the land, reproducible material capital, and labor at the disposal of these farmers are allocated quite efficiently, more so than in modern agriculture. Another hypothesis indicates that the rate of return to investment in traditional agriculture is low, which means that the incentive to expand production is weak.

Before putting these hypotheses to test, we might look more closely at the underlying economic basis. To do this we must return to the key unsettled question: Why do farmers who are bound by traditional agriculture behave as if they either cannot, or do not want to, increase production substantially over a period of time? It could be because of a lack of good land. Yet, as already noted, many of these farmers are on irrigated plains or on a delta, farming first-rate land. They also often have an impressive number of draft animals, and the labor force is as a rule large. Nor by any stretch of the imagination can it be held that their wants are satiated either for food or for products to be had in exchange for food. Thus, this is no answer to the query, "Why is traditional agriculture not substantially increasing its production?"

Nevertheless, what I have just said distinguishes between two basic explanations. One makes it a matter of *preferences* and the other is based on *production possibilities*. It could, of course, be true that both are important. The matter of preferences focuses attention on the values by which farm people measure a good life. Thus, for cultural reasons, they might prefer, for example, much leisure and little work, and more consumption relative to savings than do farm people who have entered upon modern agriculture. The widely held view that this is indeed the case is based on the belief that the low level of production is fundamentally a matter of preferences which do not favor savings nor doing the extra work that would be required to increase production rapidly over time.

PREFERENCES

Much of our trouble in understanding agriculture in poor countries arises from misconceptions of the preferences of the people concerned and of the role of preferences in economic behavior. It is fashionable to attribute to them preferences which characterize them as indolent, as squanderers, and as unfit culturally to modernize. According to this fashion, what must come first is a cultural reform. Some economists have even dropped their tools to march in this reform movement. But the analytical core of economics cannot provide a basis for such cultural reforms; economists are not experts on how to change people's preferences and personalities; farm people in traditional societies are not indifferent to earnings from work and to returns from investment; and these people have long had a bad press.

Economics is not equipped to distinguish between inferior and superior preferences, or to determine the value of one set of preferences over another. It takes preferences as given. They are what they are because of people's values. Preferences, however, have particular properties, and the tools of economics are designed to identify and measure the effects of these properties as they are revealed by people in their behavior.

Selling Economics Short

Yet some economists have abandoned this approach to preferences. Their aim is to improve the preferences of people in poor countries. They are predominantly concerned, so it seems, with cultural issues beyond economics. This shift away from economic issues, in my view, has been a serious mistake, because however competent they are as economists, they are at best amateur anthropologists or sociologists; and in making this shift they neglect the economic aspects, some of which really matter. I hasten to say that I am not against specialization. Quite the contrary, I see real gains to be had from specialization by economists, qua economic analysis.

What I mean can be illustrated by referring to Professor Everett E. Hagen's scholarly book, *On the Theory of Social Change.*[3] This book is devoted mainly to the *personality* of people in traditional societies. It concentrates on the social structure; the role of rationality, religion, and magic; the elite sense of identity; and the role of authority. It then goes on to authoritarian and innovational personalities and the formation of these types. In discussing the transition to economic growth, it stresses the withdrawal of status respect and the emergence of technological creativity. But nowhere does Professor Hagen bring his well-known competence as an economist to bear analytically, for the simple reason that his study goes far beyond the realm where the tools of economics have relevance. I am, of course, not implying that economists can afford to overlook the studies of scholars in other disciplines. I for one have found the work of some anthropologists especially rewarding, as is evident in my *Transforming Traditional Agriculture*[4] in which I drew heavily upon *Penny Capitalism*[5] by Sol Tax, and on a study of Senapur[6] by

W. David Hopper. In another field Gordon Wright, the historian, in his *Rural Revolution in France*[7] contributes much that is useful to economists. Moreover, it seems to be true that those who specialize in some of the other social disciplines can enter upon the elementary aspects of economics more efficiently than economists can enter their fields of endeavor. The reason for this may be that anthropology, for example, is based on a conception of cultural behavior which includes as one of its subsets, economic behavior. In any event, Tax and Hopper even concentrated on these economic aspects and in a surprisingly sure-footed manner, although there are others who have slipped in taking this step.[8]

Grist for Economics

If farm people in traditional societies were indifferent to all economic choices, economic analysis would be irrelevant. If they were to place a very low value on the components of economic growth, economics could contribute precious little. Thus, if they really prefer an inordinate amount of idleness (much time for leisure regardless of earnings) and a rate of consumption that leaves little or no surplus for savings, regardless of the profitability of investment opportunities, and if such idleness and such indifference to investment opportunities were the basic reasons for the poor performance of this type of agriculture in terms of increasing production, then indeed we are confronted primarily by cultural problems which are beyond the economic calculus. But this hopeless view of preferences of farm people in traditional agriculture is altogether unwarranted. They are not indifferent to the prices of products, or to earnings from work, or to rates of return from investment. Thus, there is grist here for the economist's mill.

I am not implying that there are no cultural restraints which to some extent hinder economic growth and are beyond economics. Let me mention some of the more obvious ones. Science and the attributes of scientific thinking are lacking in varying degrees, caste arrangements and some extended family systems restrict the choices of people, some land-tenure arrangements that are deeply imbedded culturally blunt economic incentives, manual work and especially farm work are often held in low regard, and there has been little opportunity to learn what the economic value of schooling is as part of the process of economic growth. Yet despite these cultural limitations there is much scope for economic analysis in pointing the way for modernizing traditional agriculture efficiently.

The Two Myths

There is the myth that people in traditional societies, notably farm people, have a strong penchant for being idle. We are told repeatedly that they do not want to work hard or long because they have the preferences of inveterate loafers. But what superficial observers call loafing is predominantly a consequence of the low marginal productivity of labor. The very low productivity of labor also accounts in large part for the poverty. The other myth is that these people have a low regard for thrift. They, so the literature runs, prefer to indulge in much wasteful consumption: for well-to-do landowners it is a way of life, and for poor farmers it is mandatory when marriage and death occur and when festivals come along. They therefore, so it is said, fail to save enough to get ahead. But what has been overlooked is the low marginal rate of return to be had on their savings. There is thus little or no inducement to save.

A Bad Press

Farm people in traditional agriculture have long had a bad press which has featured them as indolent by nature and squanderers by taste. Little wonder that the leaders of most of the new nations have placed their bets on industry—above all on steel mills. The authorities in Soviet-type countries for quite other reasons deeply distrust farm people politically. Marx, too, distrusted the lowly peasant who refuses to play the historical game of economic materialism according to Marxian rules. Hume, Smith, and Ricardo viewed agriculture as the sinecure of an unprogressive landed aristocracy opposed to manufacturing and commerce. Presumably anyone who is associated with agriculture is suspect! Hume goes so far as to accuse farm people of having a predisposition to indolence. His defamation of them is terse: "A habit of indolence naturally prevails. The greater part of the land lies uncultivated. What is cultivated, yields not its utmost for want of skill and assiduity in the farmers."[9] Those who were thus libeled were, of course, in no position to obtain relief. Unchallenged, Hume called them not only indolent but also squanderers of their economic surplus. Since rent from land was viewed as the principal source of such a surplus, the landed proprietors bear the onus of not saving and investing this surplus. They dissipate it because, said Hume, "spending of a settled revenue is a way of life . . . pleasures, such as they are, will be the pursuit of the greater part of the landholders . . . as there is little frugality."[10]

Thus indolence and profligacy are clichés in the bad press that has been the lot of farm people in traditional societies. True, the libel of indolence appears less frequently now, as a consequence of the advances made in treating "attitudes toward work," exemplified in the writing of W. Arthur Lewis.[11] But even Lewis repeats the old aspersion that these farmers are squanderers for he says: "Large rent incomes do not result in saving because a landed aristocracy does not think in terms of using its income for productive investment. . . . The same goes for the peasant class . . . those peasants who save tend to invest either in lending to less fortunate peasants, or else in buying more land, and in neither case is the result an increase in capital formation."[12]

Let me be sure I am not misunderstood with respect to industrialization, the role of political power in the Soviet Union, and landowners. Although the allegation that farm people in poor countries are innately indolent and squanderers is patently false, it is nevertheless true that these countries should industrialize. But they should also modernize their agriculture instead of neglecting it, or even worse, attempting to industrialize at the expense of agriculture. In the case of the Soviet Union, no doubt those in authority have good reasons for distrusting farm people. But the Soviet organization of agriculture, while it assures the government of political control, is not an efficient economic organization either for current production or for modernizing agriculture. Farms now consist of giants and pygmies; there are 51,000 collective and state farms with fleets of big tractors, and 30,000,000 plot farms on which work is done with many hoes.[13] Both are absurd economic types. The Marxian tenet that ever-larger farms will reduce the costs of agricultural products is not based on economic logic, and it is in want of empirical support. With respect to private landlords, a landed aristocracy is nowhere renowned for its progressive economic performance. Our own history bears convincing testimony with respect to the baneful influence that it has had on the economic development of the South. In shaping the *Southern Tradition* it has been most unprogressive, for example, in the low value that it has placed upon public schools. Its social rigidity, undemocratic political structure, and weak social responsibility, as these bear on economic progress, are clearly shown by W. H. Nicholls.[14] As for absentee landlords, they are in general less efficient than resident farmers in making current operating and investment decisions not only because of the many decisions which entail spatial, seasonal, weather, and biological subtleties which cannot be routinized, but also because of decisions that are required in adopting and learning how to use efficiently the new, superior agricultural inputs that are developed as a consequence of the advance in knowledge.[15]

Thus, to summarize with respect to preferences, the fashionable view that farm people in traditional societies are indifferent to earnings from work and to rates of return from investment is wrong. Because it is wrong, there is a role for economic analysis. True, there are some cultural restraints which have some adverse effects on production, yet despite these there is much room for economic progress. When economists argue for cultural reforms to change preferences they enter upon issues that go far beyond economics. A libelous press has long maligned farm people in traditional societies, repeatedly relating accounts of their indolence and improvidence.

PRODUCTION POSSIBILITIES

Here, too, we are in trouble because of an array of misconceptions. The most common mistake is to overrate the production possibilities in agriculture in these countries and then conclude that farmers are incompetent because they produce much less than we presume to be readily possible. When we see that not all of the available water is used, we are sure they are wasteful without bothering to examine the costs and returns from using the water. We make the same mistake when we observe that they do not apply fertilizer. Low yields are attributed to a lack of entrepreneurship and not to the niggardly production possibilities, which are the real reason. We apply the dubious notion of "disguised unemployment" to their situation and then assert that many farm workers are wholly redundant; the convenient figure is that 25 percent of those who want to work, who are capable of working, and who are in fact working contribute nothing to production. I have shown elsewhere that this doctrine must be discarded for want of theoretical and empirical support.[16]

Why are these agricultural production possibilities so niggardly? The reasons have been briefly stated in Chapter I. In this type of agriculture, farmers have long ago exhausted the productivity of the state of the arts at their disposal. They have carried production to the point where the marginal returns from additional work and from investment to improve the land and to acquire more draft animals and other reproducible inputs are too low to warrant the extra work and savings. Another closely related reason is that they have learned over many generations how to allocate the agricultural factors at their disposal so that there are few significant inefficiencies. Changes in products and factors have not crowded in on them as is typical of modern farming. On the contrary, because the state of the arts on which their farming is based has remained virtually constant for generations, they have made the best of it. As W. David Hopper observed in Senapur: "The age-old techniques have been refined and sharpened by countless years of experience, and each generation seems to have had its experimenters who added a bit here and changed a practice there, and thus improved the community lore. Rotations, tillage, and cultivation practices, seed rates, irrigation techniques, and the ability of the blacksmith and potter to work under handicaps of little power and inferior materials, all attest to a cultural heritage that is richly endowed with empirical wisdom."[17] Thus, one would be surprised to find that they had not attained a high level of efficiency in allocating the agricultural factors at their disposal.

In turning to a systematic examination of the evidence it may be noted that it consists of three parts, namely, the supply response of farmers in traditional agriculture, the comparative efficiency with which they allocate the agricultural resources at their disposal, and the low marginal rates of return to investment when it is undertaken to increase the capacity of agriculture.

SUPPLY RESPONSE

Suppose these farmers did not respond to economic incentives. Then there would be no basis for believing that they maximize the returns to be had from their resources except by sheer accident. Although the refrain that farmers in poor countries do not respond to economic incentives is still very popular,[18] it is being interrupted by strong evidence to the contrary.

The corn boom in Thailand represents a remarkable response to new economic opportunities: production rose sevenfold between 1956 and 1961, from 115,000 to 800,000 tons, and corn which had accounted for only 1 percent jumped to over 6 percent of total agricultural output.[19] Purchases by Japan made corn prices profitable, and farmers in Thailand responded promptly by planting more and by increasing yields markedly.[20]

Long overlooked is the supply response of farmers in northern Sudan in producing beans for sale, which increased fivefold from 1948 to 1955 as prices rose, and which then fell by nearly one-half in two years following a sharp decline in prices.[21] The supply responses of Mexican farmers in cotton, wheat, and corn are noteworthy. Nor should the farm supply response in Ghana of cocoa beans and that of cotton in a number of Latin American countries be overlooked. Since many Indian economists have been especially fond of the refrain that prices do not matter, the recent expansion in sugarcane production at the expense of rice and other food crops in India should give them pause; among other things sugarcane producers, induced by profits, have even managed to acquire more than their share of the planned distribution of fertilizer.[22]

Three recent econometric studies, two at Chicago and one at Harvard, represent a major advance analytically. Venkataramanan[23] found that for jute in India between 1911 and 1938 the coefficient of adjustment was 0.64 and the short-run and long-run elasticities 0.46 and 0.73. These are impressively large coefficients with respect to farmers' responses. Krishna,[24] concentrating on nine crops grown in the Punjab region, leaves little room for doubt that Punjab farmers can adjust and that they do respond to price incentives. Comparing his estimates with Nerlove's estimates for the United States, Krishna concludes "that while the elasticity of the acreage of wheat in the Punjab was much lower than in the United States, the elasticities of cotton and maize acreage in the Punjab were significantly higher. This is a remarkable result for a poor economy like that of the Punjab in the inter-war period."[25] Falcon[26] in a case study of West Pakistan obtained estimates that are consistent with those of Krishna. The relevance and importance of these estimates are summarized by Krishna: "The rapidity of adjustment of the acreage of crops by the peasants in response to changing circumstances is not very different from that estimated for the United States. The Punjab peasants were evidently not unusually tardy in adjusting fairly 'rationally' to changes in their economic environment."[27]

THE ALLOCATIVE TEST

By the allocative test I mean the achievement of an optimum rate of output from given factors of production. Accordingly, the better the collection of factors, the larger the output, provided the level of efficiency is the same. Thus, the fact that Japanese farmers produce much more than farmers in India is no proof that the Japanese are the more efficient. In Japan irrigation facilities are much superior, the supply of fertilizer is also better and far cheaper relative to the price of rice, vastly better seeds have been developed than India has, and what is exceedingly important, Japanese farmers have a much higher level of skills. Even if the Japanese were quite inefficient in using the high quality agricultural inputs now at their disposal, they could still produce a great deal more per acre, per worker, and per farm, no matter how efficient the Indians were. I do not wish to imply that Japanese farmers are inefficient. What I want to make clear is that the low level of productivity in countries such as India is no proof that farmers in these countries are inefficient in using the factors of production available to them.

Sol Tax's classic study[28] of a very poor farming community in Guatemala provides abundant evidence that these Indians made every penny count in allocating the resources on which they were dependent.[29] W. David Hopper made a strong test of the allocation hypothesis here under consideration. This test is based on his data for Senapur, India.[30] He took the prices of farm products and of the factors of production that prevailed at the time. He then estimated the prices that were implicit in their production activities, that is, in the marginal returns from the way they allocated the resources which they had. He found "a remarkably close correspondence between" the real prices that prevailed and the prices implicit in what they did. The farmers of Senapur were impressively efficient in this sense. It would be rare to find farmers in Europe, the United States, or elsewhere in modern agriculture who were equally efficient in using the resources at their command, and for obvious reasons—the rapidly changing economic conditions.

Why then the widely held belief that the output of traditional agriculture would increase markedly if farmers were only more efficient? The answer is that we have been trapped by our misconceptions. The role of farm management is a case in point. While it has made many contributions which have improved the decisions of our farmers in adjusting to new economic opportunities, such opportunities simply do not exist in traditional agriculture. Another misconception is that there is much to be gained from imitating the "best" farmers. One can always find some farmers who are producing more than the rest. But what is often overlooked is the real difference between them in the quality and quantity of agricultural resources. My comment on why it is inappropriate to compare the output of Japanese and Indian farmers for this purpose is also applicable here. What is also overlooked is the fact that during the early years when we relied heavily in our extension work on the practices of the "best" farmers to assist other farmers in increasing their yields, very little was achieved.

If it were true that a part of the labor in farming were redundant, it would undermine my hypothesis. But this doctrine of labor of zero value is demonstrably wrong.[31] If there were marked disparities in returns to comparable inputs, with product and factor prices given, it also would count against the allocative efficiency hypothesis here advanced. Where this inference has been drawn, it turns out to be a very doubtful inference, because the inputs were not comparable or because the particular farmers were in process of adjusting to a change in economic conditions.

PROFITABILITY OF INVESTMENT

Based on the concept that traditional agriculture is a long-established economic equilibrium, we derived the hypothesis that the rate of return to investment is low. To test this hypothesis it is necessary to distinguish between two classes of inputs: (1) inputs that farmers are accustomed to, that is, precisely the same type of irrigation wells and ditches, draft animals, implements, seeds, and so on used by farmers for generations; and (2) a wide array of other inputs including modern inputs that are not available to them and therefore not relevant as they make their investment decisions. In testing this hypothesis we must also leave aside communities in which off-farm changes have altered product and factor prices, for example, the effects on nearby agriculture of a new highway to which farmers are in process of adjusting.

I need a *bench mark* by which to measure a low rate of return, in surveying this field. I shall use a 10 percent rate of return as such a bench mark. Since the rate that can be observed is always subject to some risk and uncertainty, any expected rate of return that is less than this is, as a rule, a weak inducement for economic growth. Thus, rates as low as 3 or 4 percent provide little or no inducement for entrepreneurs to invest. Conversely, when the expected rates rise to 10 percent and more the stage is set for substantial economic growth.[32]

As we take our bearing, let me first mention two specific cases where investment in what had been traditional agriculture became highly profitable. A new paved highway joining Brasilia, the new capital city of Brazil, and São Paulo runs through an agricultural area that had been substantially isolated and thus for reasons of high transport costs only sparsely settled. The new road in effect opened this fairly large area, for it made farming in it highly profitable with rates of return of 20 percent and more.[33] The response has been akin to a gold rush. In Mexico new large public irrigation facilities in the northeast have undoubtedly produced very high rates of returns, and agriculture has responded accordingly.

In turning to investment in traditional agriculture that is restricted to reproducible capital forms of the customary types, we may consider India, where there has been much irrigation for generations. Were there still large unexploited investment opportunities—for example, at the time India attained independence? Except for new cheaper sources of power to lift water from wells and for a few remaining first-rate dam sites that had not been developed, investment in irrigation facilities had long ago reduced the marginal rate of return to a low level. Yet the government of India has been investing heavily in more irrigation, a traditional way of increasing agricultural production. Has it been highly profitable? The answer is, no. On the contrary, the payoff appears to be very low.

The economic history of long-settled agricultural communities—especially where there is irrigation—indicates that a surprisingly large stock of reproducible capital has been formed by investment. Senapur, India, which in 1957 had only 1064 acres, nevertheless had 750 "productive" animals of which 480 were bullocks for field work. For irrigation it had 266 wells and 76 tanks for storing water. A comparison of agricultural inputs in the United States and in irrigated agriculture in the Punjab is instructive on this point. In the United States power and machinery comprise about 26 percent of all inputs; in the Punjab bullocks and implements represent 30 percent of all inputs. Reproducible nonhuman capital in both the U.S. and the Punjab is slightly more than 50 percent of the total input. Thus, clearly traditional agriculture so situated has been saving and investing and over decades has accumulated a large stock of reproducible capital. There is little room for doubt that the rate of return to additional investment in types of capital customarily employed has become very low. As of 1957 farmers in Senapur could not have earned anywhere near a 10 percent rate of return by investing in a few more wells, or tanks, or bullocks.

Another indication of low rates of return is in the experience of farmer cooperatives in poor countries in which they serve as savings banks. Although they pay only a modest rate of interest on the savings that farmer members deposit with them it is noteworthy that farmers deposit savings instead of investing them in farming, thus supporting the inference that the low rate of interest is more attractive than what they could earn were they to invest, for example, in another bullock.

My estimate of the net rate of return to land, implicit in the data of *Penny Capitalism* (Panajachel, Guatemala), is 4 percent or less.[34] Hopper's more rigorous test for Senapur indicates that the marginal product of land was equal to about 3 percent of the then prevailing price of land.[35]

NECESSARY CONCLUSIONS

Traditional agriculture is not capable of contributing cheaply to economic growth because it has exhausted the economic opportunities of the state of the arts on which it is dependent.

The key to this lack in capability, therefore, is not a matter of allocative efficiency. The many efforts to show farmers in traditional agriculture how to use more efficiently the resources which they have are in vain, because they are in this respect essentially efficient.

Nor is this lack in capability a matter of simply investing more in what they have. Thus, our efforts to induce them to invest more than they are investing in the factors of production available to them are also in vain; the investment opportunities open to them simply do not warrant their doing so.

Why, then, do we try so hard in vain? The answer is that we are victims of our misconceptions. We hold fast to the erroneous beliefs that these farmers are thriftless, bad entrepreneurs, and predisposed to be loafers. Our image of them is that they lack the propensity to save and the willingness to work hard and long, that they are indifferent to economic incentives, and that they are subject to cultural restraints which leave no room for economic progress. Thus, we are trapped by an array of misconceptions.

The conclusion that really matters from this approach is a theory of economic growth from traditional agriculture, a theory that clearly indicates where to look for relatively cheap sources of additional agricultural production, a theory of investment which concentrates on high payoff new inputs, a theory of investment in both material and human capital to improve the state of the arts, which is the only real source of new profitable investment opportunities.

Once we are clear with respect to the full implication of this theory and let it guide us in what we do abroad to assist poor countries, agriculture will become for them a relatively cheap source of economic growth. Only then will the age-old anxiety of their people concerning food recede and disappear.

III

Economic Growth from Traditional Agriculture[1]

Whatever the reason, it is much easier for a poor country to acquire a modern steel mill than a modern agriculture. When it wants a steel mill, whether for production or for prestige, it can turn to Europeans, Russians, or Americans with assurance that it will get what it wants. But when it wants a modern agriculture that will be successful, to whom can a poor country turn with confidence. To the Soviet Union? Surely this would be carrying ideology too far. Of course, the place to turn is to one of the countries in which agriculture is making a large contribution to economic growth. Thus the United States qualifies. Our product is modern agriculture and we are in the export business. But our product has not performed well abroad. What are the reasons?

Why are we, as builders of agriculture, not skilled in undertaking this task abroad? We are renowned for our land-grant agricultural colleges, experiment stations, extension services, and the U.S.D.A. We place a high value on the industries that supply agricultural inputs and that process and distribute farm products, on the network of communications that serves farm people, and on the abilities of farmers,

41

although we often overlook the importance of the schooling of farm people. Yet, seemingly, we do not know how to institutionalize this type of a public-private approach abroad.

It cannot be said that the United States has not been trying to help poor countries modernize their agriculture, for we have committed large sums and much talent to this task. Our government for over two decades has been engaged in technical assistance to agriculture. Our principal foundations have been pioneers. Our agricultural colleges have undertaken counterpart work abroad. We are involved in country planning to achieve, among other things, increases in agricultural production. We are also involved in land reform, the establishment of rural credit institutions, community development programs and other types of agricultural extension services, technical assistance to agriculture, university contracts, and an array of specialized training programs. But despite all of these programs and this talent, the fact is that these approaches have so far not achieved results that come even close to expectations. There is understandably a growing doubt both among ourselves and among leaders abroad whether we are efficient in these matters. What accounts for this apparent lack of success?

One difficulty in answering this question is that there are all too many explanations. There are those who believe our lack of success stems from our failure to understand the real basis of the success of agriculture in the United States. It could be that we have as yet not identified the institutional components that matter most. It could also be true that we have had wholly unwarranted expectations as to what can be accomplished in any short period of time. The way we reckon costs and returns may be inadequate, and therefore the test of our efficiency may be defective. But regardless of the source of the difficulty, some programs are undoubtedly better than others. Meanwhile, the present danger is that since we and the governments concerned are unable to rate these programs correctly, even the best of them may lose support or even be discontinued altogether. It is therefore imperative that we take stock. What then accounts for this lack of success?

To find an answer to this question and to indicate what needs to be done I shall:

Restate the economic basis implicit in what I presented in Chapter I.

Show where private profit activities require complementary public activities.

Establish the reasons for the lack of success of most programs to modernize agriculture in poor countries.

Present the requirements for an efficient approach.

ECONOMIC BASIS AGAIN

First, farmers in poor countries are in general *not inefficient* in using (allocating) the agricultural factors of production that they have at their disposal. Their preferences for acquiring and holding wealth, which appear to be essentially the same as those of modern farmers, and the state of the arts to which they are bound, have remained virtually constant for generations. As a consequence they have long since attained a type of economic equilibrium. Thus, the popular presumption that a better allocation of the existing poor collection of agricultural factors in these communities would substantially increase agricultural production is inconsistent both with economic logic applied to the behavior of farmers in such an equilibrium and with the available empirical evidence. Strange as it may seem, it is true that on the basis of a strict allocative test, these farmers are more efficient than farmers in most of modern agriculture, because the latter are in a state of disequilibrium, a consequence of their "rapid progress."

Second, when it comes to investment to increase agricultural production, farmers who are bound by traditional agriculture have in general exhausted all profitable opportunities to invest in the agricultural factors at their disposal. This means that the marginal rate of return to investment in agricultural factors of the type which farmers have long been using is low, so low that there is little or no incentive to save and invest. Therefore, economic growth from traditional agriculture is very expensive. It means, in practical terms, that adding a few more wells and ditches for irrigation, several more draft animals and implements, and other forms of reproducible capital of the type farmers have been using for generations will increase agricultural production very little, so little in fact that it yields an unattractive rate of return.

These two economic properties are basic in understanding the behavior of farmers in traditional agriculture. What they imply for economic growth from agriculture in many poor countries is both real and relevant. Programs aimed solely at improving the economic efficiency of farmers are doomed to fail. Likewise, programs designed solely to induce farmers in traditional agriculture to increase their investment in precisely the same type of agricultural factors they have been using for generations will fail; they will not be accepted simply because the payoff is too low.

What then are the rewarding sources of economic growth to be anticipated from the type of agriculture under consideration? Is it more land? In old long-settled communities with no open frontiers, additional land suitable for cultivation is hard to come by. Some, of course, will become available, for even in India it appears that a part of the recent increases in agricultural production has come from this source. But it is not likely to be nearly so important a source during the next ten years. In some parts of Latin America, notably in Brazil, new roads are opening new land for settlement. In general, however, increases in agricultural production will have to come from land already under cultivation, especially so in the long-settled poor countries.

Additional irrigation is on approximately the same footing as land. India, for example, already has three times as much land under irrigation as Japan—measured on a per capita basis. Yet India has invested large sums during recent years in still more irrigation. Had India invested enough of these sums to develop a low-cost efficient fertilizer industry, the payoff undoubtedly would have been much higher in terms of profitable increases in agricultural production. But in Mexico, which is clearly an exception in this respect, irrigation facilities have been an important source of economic growth from agriculture. Additional draft animals, implements, and related tools and facilities of the type now being used in poor countries are unpromising sources of economic growth.

It will be helpful at this point to distinguish between agricultural inputs that originate within agriculture and those supplied from outside. With few exceptions all of the inputs that farmers in poor countries can produce for themselves are low payoff sources. On the other hand, virtually all agricultural inputs that hold real promise must come from outside of agriculture. This is obvious for commercial fertilizer, machinery, tractors, insecticides, and the development of genetically superior plants and animals. While less obvious, it is also true for schooling and other means to improve the skills of farm people.

The high payoff sources are predominantly *improvements in the quality of agricultural inputs;* these inputs can be acquired by farmers only from non-farm firms and from agencies engaged in agricultural research, in extension work, and in schooling. It is, therefore, necessary to develop ways and means of improving the quality not only of the material reproducible inputs but also of human agents engaged in farming. Thus far, in our attempts to assist poor countries modernize their agriculture we have been vague and uncertain with regard to these sources of economic growth, and where we have happened to concentrate on the correct objective we have—with few exceptions—failed to do things in the right order and in ways that would institutionalize the process.

The people who build steel mills for poor countries may have the easier task, but clearly they have also demonstrated that they have a better conception of what needs to be done than have those engaged in modernizing the agriculture.

PRIVATE PROFIT INCENTIVES NOT SUFFICIENT

The key to economic growth from farming is improvement in the quality of agriculture inputs and then in supplying them at a price that will make it worthwhile for farmers to acquire them and to learn how to use them efficiently. But firms for profit unassisted by research, schooling, and extension work are too weak to turn this key. What this means is that a pure market approach is not sufficient. Although there is a good deal of tilting at ideological windmills in the area of economic policy, there is fortunately little of it in the case of agricultural research, extension work, and schooling by Americans who have had their apprenticeship in institutions that serve agriculture in the United States. The reasons why the economic incentives of firms for profit throughout the nonfarm sectors are frequently weak in supplying inputs to modernize agriculture will be presented shortly.

Before turning to them, there are two preliminary issues with respect to economic incentives which I

Table 2

Fertilizer and Farm Product Prices
Comparisons by Commodities and Countries, 1960-61

	Price paid by farmers for fertilizer, 1960-61[1] (in U.S. dollars per 100 kg.)			Price received by farmers for products, 1960 (in U.S. dollars per 100 kg.)	Ratio of fertilizer price to product price		
	Nitro-genous	Phos-phate	Pot-ash		(1) (4)	(2) (4)	(3) (4)
	(1)	(2)	(3)	(4)	(5)	(6)	(7)
I WHEAT[3]							
India	37.00[4]	26.20[4]		6.75[5]	5.48	3.88	
Japan	24.70	21.90	9.20	10.40	2.38	2.11	.88
France	30.00	21.50	8.30	8.10	3.70	2.65	1.02
U.S.[2]	26.90	19.70	9.40	6.40	4.20	3.08	1.47
II RICE[6]							
India	37.00	26.20		7.80[7]	4.74	3.36	
Japan	24.70	21.90	9.20	19.30	1.28	1.13	.48
U.S.[2]	26.90	19.70	9.40	10.10	2.66	1.95	.93
III CORN[8]							
India	37.00	26.20		5.30	6.98	4.94	
U.S.[2]	26.90	19.70	9.40	4.10	6.56	4.80	2.29
IV SUGAR CANE[9]							
India	37.00	26.20		9.10	4.07	2.88	
U.S.[2]	26.90	19.70	9.40	9.50	2.83	2.07	.99

SOURCE: *FAO Production Yearbook 1961* (Rome), 15.

[1] Table 174, Prices paid by farmers for bagged fertilizer on a plant nutrient basis.

[2] Average of bagged and bulk.

[3] Producer price 1960. Table 126, FAO source.

[4] 1959-60.

must consider in order to forestall being misunderstood. By weak incentives I do not mean that farmers in poor countries are not responsive to prices. The
doctrine that farmers in poor countries either are
indifferent or respond perversely to changes in prices,
including the terms on which credit is available, as
noted, is patently false and harmful. Price policies
based on it always impair the efficiency of agriculture.

Not enough attention has been given to product
and factor prices in efforts to assist countries in modernizing their agriculture. Where product prices are
suppressed or where they thwart farmers, no program, however well conceived and administered, can
succeed. It should be obvious that where the price of
fertilizer is too high relative to the price of the farm
product, no extension program can be devised that
will induce farmers to use more fertilizer. Farmers
will not and, of course, should not apply additional
fertilizer under these circumstances. In Japan, where
farmers apply a hundred times as much fertilizer per
acre as do farmers in India, the price of fertilizer is

---

[5] 78.5 percent of the wholesale price in Table 126. See
Indian Journal of Agricultural Economics, XVII (January-
March 1962), pp. 81-84 for adjustment.

[6] Producer paddy price, 1960. Table 133, FAO source.

[7] 83 percent of the wholesale price of coarse rice shown in
Table 133. See *Indian Journal of Agricultural Economics,*
XVII (January-March 1962), Table 1, p. 48, and Appendix 1,
pp. 51-52, for adjustment, based on 1957-58, Bolpur market
seasonal distribution.

[8] Producer price 1960. Table 130, FAO source, India wholesale price adjusted to a 75 percent basis.

[9] From Table 134 of FAO source.

Table 3

Fertilizer and Rice Prices in Eight Countries, 1960-61

	Prices paid by farmers for nitrogenous fertilizer[1]	Prices received by farmers for rice[2]	Ratio $\frac{(1)}{(2)}$	Index based on Japan
				(128=100)
	(1)	(2)	(3)	(4)
Japan	$24.70	$19.30	1.28	100
Italy	21.00	9.30	2.26	177
U.S.	26.90	10.10	2.66	208
Ceylon	36.80	12.10	3.04	238
India	37.00	7.80	4.74	370
Thailand	27.90	4.30	6.49	507
U.A.R.	40.30	5.20	7.75	605
Burma	28.60	3.00	9.53	745

SOURCE: *FAO Production Yearbook 1961* (Rome), 15, Tables 133 and 174.
[1] Price in U.S. dollars per kg. paid by producers.
[2] Price received by producers. Japan includes package. Thailand is the wholesale price in Bangkok. Price in U.S. dollars per 100 kg.

vastly lower in relation to the price of farm products. It takes less than half as many pounds of wheat in Japan to buy a pound of nitrogenous fertilizer as it does in India (see Tables 2 and 3). In the case of rice, the differences in prices are even larger. Rice farmers in India pay between three and four times as much for this fertilizer as do farmers in Japan in terms of the price that they receive for rice, while the farmers in Thailand pay more than five times as much. Little wonder then that farmers in India[2] and Thailand find fertilizer unprofitable.

There are also the probable adverse effects of Public Law 480 exports, not only upon world prices but, more important in relation to the task at hand, upon farm product prices in some of the poor countries receiving large quantities of these products from the United States. Although the total quantity of resources available to the receiving country for economic growth is increased, these imports are likely to depress particular farm product prices within the receiving country below what they otherwise would have been, and to this extent the economic incentives to farmers to increase agricultural products are impaired. We need to detect and help correct the widespread underpricing of farm products and overpricing of agricultural inputs in poor countries.

The other preliminary issue pertains to the economic incentives influencing farmers who are bound by traditional agriculture, even though there are no overt policies causing the types of underpricing and overpricing referred to above. The economic basis for the observable allocative efficiency and for the unrewarding investment opportunities has already been presented. The implication is that farmers situated in such a penny economy use the existing poor collection of agricultural resources so that every penny counts; measured in economic terms, marginal costs and returns are equated exceedingly fine. These farmers, accordingly, have exhausted for all practical purposes the gains to be had from economic efficiency. They also have exhausted the gains to be had from additional investment in agricultural factors of production of the type that have long been at their disposal. The state of the arts available to them has been pursued to its outer limit in equating with a penny fineness marginal preferences to save and marginal rates of return to investment.

Now, as to the key issue, why is it that firms for profit unassisted by nonprofit agencies that concentrate on agricultural research, extension work, and schooling are not capable of modernizing agriculture efficiently? The answer is really quite simple. The benefits from these activities accrue in substantial part to individuals and firms other than those who produce them. This means that if firms for profit were to undertake them, they would be saddled with all the costs but would not be able to capture all the returns. Therefore, they would enter upon agricultural research, schooling, and extension work only up to the point at which that part of the marginal returns which accrued to them would cover their marginal costs. Since there are substantial additional social returns which firms for profit cannot capture, it is a mistake to expect such firms to pursue these activities to their social optimum. Clearly then, the basic economic reason why firms for profit cannot attain a social optimum in this respect is simply a consequence of the fact that it is impossible for them to capture all of the benefits that flow from these particular activities.

I began with a judgment that as builders of agriculture we have not done well in poor countries. But have our agricultural programs abroad really been as unsuccessful as I have implied? I would be the first to concede that the available evidence is not good enough for strong inferences. Relevant data are hard to come by. It is unfortunately true that no one has had the foresight to see the experimental nature of these programs, and thus no one has kept the necessary records that would provide a basis for drawing strong inferences from these experiments.

But there is some evidence to back my judgment. It is implicit in the weak association between increases in agricultural production in foreign countries and what we have been doing for agriculture in these countries. With one or two exceptions, the most impressive increases in agricultural production since the war have occurred in countries where we have had no programs. Japan and Israel have been among the most successful. So have Austria and Greece in the Western European complex (see Table 4). Our aid to Greece undoubtedly contributed somewhat to the recent upsurge in agriculture there. In Mexico, which has a good record of economic growth from agriculture, there is, of course, a real connection between the agricultural research with which The Rockefeller Foundation has been identified and the increases in agricultural production. The Philippines and Taiwan, where we have had a substantial hand,

Table 4

Country and Regional Increases in Agricultural Production: Total and per Capita—1935-39 to 1962

	TOTAL		PER CAPITA	
	1935-39	1962	1935-39	1962
				(Cols. (1) and (2)
	(1952-53 to		divided by a 1953=100	
	1954-55=100)		population index)	
	(1)	(2)	(3)	(4)
Japan	83	159	102	146
Taiwan	89	144	144	107
Philippines	73	143	104	108
India	83	130	102	107
Pakistan	103	121	126	100
(South Asia and Far East)	88	133	110	111
Mexico	47	157[1]	70	126[1]
Brazil	73	150[1]	106	116[1]
Colombia	64	124[1]	91	99[1]
Chile	73	118[1]	99	91[1]
Peru	61	117[1]	82	98[1]
(Latin America)	72	129[2]	103	101[2]
Israel	70	212[2]	115	155[2]
Turkey	66	122[2]	90	95[2]
(West Asia)	69	129[2]	97	101[2]
	Prewar		*Prewar*	
Austria	94	137[2]	97	135[2]
Greece	85	135[2]	103	125[2]
(Western Europe)	81	121[2]	92	113[2]

SOURCE: Based on Supplements to *The 1963 World Agricultural Situation*, U.S.D.A.; and "Indices of Agricultural Production for the 20 Latin American Countries," Foreign Agric. Service, U.S.D.A. (October 1959).

[1] 1961-62. [2] 1962-63.

are often cited as countries which have done well. Total agricultural production has, indeed, risen more there than in most countries, but on a per capita basis it increased only 4 percent in the Philippines, while it declined substantially in Taiwan. In India and Pakistan, where our commitments of both public and private funds and of talent have been large, the agricultural sector has had a poor record. On a per capita basis, India's agricultural production is only slightly above the prewar level and that of Pakistan is down considerably.

A few years ago with some of my colleagues I investigated the effects of technical assistance programs under way in Latin America upon the economy of these countries.[3] The U.S. Point Four program began in Latin America. From 1943 to 1955 the United States contributed $44,000,000 to agriculture and natural resource programs in Latin America, and the annual rate of our expenditures for this purpose rose to $9,000,000. Although the United States has continued to support such technical assistance programs since then, estimates of the amounts spent for agriculture are not at hand. The production effects of these programs during the years from 1943 to 1954 should have become evident during the period since then. While it is true that agricultural production in Latin America as a whole has continued to increase, the increase has been at a rate no higher than that of population. On a per capita basis between 1953 and 1961-62 nine of these countries lost ground; in two of them we had no programs (Argentina and Uruguay); and among the other seven were Chile, Colombia, Costa Rica, Paraguay, and Peru, in each of which we had large agricultural technical assistance programs. Among the eleven countries that gained somewhat on a per capita basis, one had not received technical assistance from the United States for agriculture (Venezuela), and in two of the others per capita agricultural production has risen very little (Haiti and Dominican Republic). This evidence, it seems to me, suggests a weak association between our programs to modernize agriculture and the increases in agricultural production that have been realized.

Why is the record no better than this? The answer depends upon one's conception of the task, and there are answers in profusion. Each is based on a particular view and a bit of experience, for we are above all practical, relying heavily upon pragmatic wisdom, and our wisdom is based on a wide array of experiences. But such wisdom is often swamped by extraneous considerations for lack of a general theory to guide decisions and to evaluate what we have done.

A part of the difficulty also stems from a confusion between means and end. Yet it should be obvious that the basic objective is not a set of new agricultural institutions per se; these modernizing institutions are warranted only where they become a source of economic growth from agriculture. Nor is it sufficient by this test to show that agricultural production has increased as a consequence of these institutions. It is also necessary to show that in terms of costs and returns they are a relatively cheap source of economic growth—more precisely, that they are at least not more expensive than the next best alternative source open to the country.

A theory of economic growth from agriculture, which I set forth earlier, provides an analytical basis for evaluating what we have done. The important implications of this theory can be stated very simply.

1. Many farmers in poor countries are under the economic restraints of traditional agriculture. Wherever agricultural extension programs have been launched, based on the assumption that these farmers are necessarily inefficient in allocating the agricultural factors at their disposal, it is highly probable that the programs have not contributed and cannot contribute to economic growth.

2. There are also agricultural extension and rural credit programs which are based on the belief that farmers in poor countries are not saving and investing enough of their income in agriculture and that they are using less than an optimum amount of credit. What has been overlooked in launching these programs is the fact that there are no rewarding investment opportunities open to farmers within the economic confines of traditional agriculture. Therefore, it is not possible by means of such programs to win economic growth from this type of agriculture.

3. Many of the agricultural extension programs abroad with which we are identified are attempting to induce farmers to adopt and use one or more new agricultural inputs that simply are not productive enough to make it worthwhile for farmers to introduce and use them. In the case of such new agricul-

tural inputs, including techniques and practices, farmers are not innately averse to improving their lot, but they are reacting correctly because of the small, or zero, or even minus rewards that can be realized from such inputs. Therefore, there can be little or no economic growth from such programs.

4. In short, it is highly probable that in the vast majority of situations where farmers in poor countries are not responding to our agricultural approaches no really profitable or rewarding new agricultural inputs have been *developed* and *produced* and *supplied* to farmers cheaply enough to make it worth their while to adopt them and learn how to use them efficiently. This lack of profitable new agricultural inputs is the crux of the matter. Where such inputs have become available to farmers, for example, in Mexico, farmers have responded, and one observes substantial economic growth from the agricultural sector.

The lack of success under consideration is, therefore, probably not a consequence of the long list of conventional reasons that clutter the literature on this issue. By this I mean that it is probably not because the U.S. workers in agricultural extension abroad are inadequately trained in soils, crops, animal husbandry and farm management. It is not because they do not stay abroad long enough, nor because their activities are badly organized and insufficiently integrated into the culture of the farm community. Although rural credit facilities may be meager, they are not necessarily a primary factor until new highly productive agricultural inputs become available; it is then that credit begins to count. Farms may be exceedingly small, but this too does not account for the lack of success. Nor is it because farmers in these countries are not industrious and thrifty and lack entrepreneurship. These programs are unsuccessful primarily because no profitable, rewarding new agricultural inputs have been available to farmers which they could adopt and use.

AN EFFICIENT APPROACH

What then is the time and place for extension, research, schools, and firms for profit? Is there a natural order? In what respects are they competitive or complementary? Reflections on these issues will help us see the requirements for an efficient approach. Simply pressing for more agricultural production regardless of costs is no solution. Costs must be reckoned against returns which become streams of income. Thus, additional income is the economic aim and the critical question is at what price. Accordingly, the economic test is in the price of the sources of such income streams whether from farming or from any other activity. A high price, which is characteristic of traditional agriculture, discourages investment to expand production. It follows that one of the requirements for modernizing agriculture is a supply of low-priced sources. In modern agriculture the suppliers of these sources are a mixed group consisting of firms that operate for profit and of public and private nonprofit agencies. The demanders of these sources in the first instance are farmers—who are dependent upon information in order to learn about these sources. An efficient approach, therefore, is one that organizes these firms, farms, and agencies—functioning as suppliers and demanders of new sources of income from agriculture—so that they achieve an optimum rate of economic growth.

A concept of economic growth which underlies this analysis indicates that the programs to modernize agriculture successfully must be built on the following foundation:

First, new agricultural inputs that have a relatively high payoff are required.

Second, a supply of these inputs must be available to farmers.

Third, as farmers accept them they must learn how to use them efficiently.

With regard to the first part of the foundation, the implication is that any program to modernize agriculture must begin with agricultural inputs (sometimes referred to loosely as practices and techniques) that are unmistakably rewarding. Such inputs consist predominantly of particular quality components which become an integral part of material inputs and of human agents. These quality components are embedded in tools, machines, chemicals, soil structures, and the genetic attributes of plants and animals. They also enter through an array of new skills acquired by farm people. That such rewarding inputs are an essential part of the foundation seems obvious. Yet there is little doubt that most of our lack of success on behalf of agriculture abroad can be traced back to a failure to provide this part of the foundation.

Where are these high payoff inputs to be found? We have relied heavily on three sources: (1) on the practices of the more successful farmers in the country, (2) on inputs recommended by the agricultural research establishment of the country, and (3) on inputs that are profitable in agriculture in the United States. Unfortunately, they have been mostly dry wells.

Should this not have been anticipated? Yes, we should have foreseen it with respect to the first two in view of our experiences in the United States. High payoff agricultural inputs with rare exceptions have not been discovered and developed by our best farmers. The early corn yield tests, which were based on searching for superior seed corn on Iowa farms for twelve years from 1904 to 1915 and testing these seeds on 75,000 field plots, as summarized by Martin L. Mosher,[4] indicate how slow and difficult it was to improve corn yields by this approach—even with exceptionally competent and inspired workers and leadership. Corn yields in Iowa which had averaged 32.4 bushels an acre from 1896 to 1905 averaged only 33 bushels during 1913, 1914, and 1915.

Nor has our own agricultural research establishment always provided a stream of new, high payoff agricultural inputs. While it has been doing so since about the middle of the 1920's, we have been blind to the fact that for decades prior to that, it produced a trickle that is hard to detect. Increases in agricultural production between 1900 and 1925 can be entirely accounted for by increases in conventional agricultural inputs. The rate of increase in agricultural output was small, about 0.9 percent a year while conventional agriculture inputs rose 1.0 percent a year.[5] Thus, we might well have been on our guard and not have taken it for granted that the agricultural experiment stations in India, or in Latin America, or elsewhere in poor countries had already discovered and developed a supply of high payoff agricultural inputs awaiting to be adopted by farmers. Although there may be some exceptions, in general these agricultural experiment stations have not as yet produced large successes; in this respect they are at a stage that is comparable to our own between 1900 and 1925.

How little or how much can be accomplished by transferring particular agricultural inputs that are highly productive and rewarding in the United States is undoubtedly something we had to learn largely from experience. Be that as it may, the tuition has been high, but we now know that such direct transfers are not a rewarding source of agricultural inputs for poor countries.

There is, however, a fourth source, namely new agricultural research. But why should it be any more fruitful than the old agricultural research already considered? The reason is fairly obvious. There have been important recent advances in scientific knowledge consisting of theories and principles that have been tested and found useful. Research based on these theories and principles is full of promise. Not that they will suffice in coping with all phases of tropical agriculture; nevertheless, they represent a major scientific asset waiting to be mobilized. But such new agricultural research has been grossly neglected in what has been done for agriculture abroad.

Although our government has been actively engaged in technical assistance for agriculture throughout Latin America for two decades, the sad truth is that not a single first-class agricultural research center has been developed as a consequence of these activities. Mexico has done well, but not because of any technical assistance from the United States government. The funds and talent provided by The Rockefeller Foundation have, however, played a part in the Mexican advance. Japan has done exceedingly well on her own. But throughout South Asia, where we have both public and private commitments to assist agriculture, with few exceptions new agricultural research has been neglected. The new research to develop superior wheat, corn, and grain sorghum varieties in India and the recently established International Rice Research Institute in the Philippines are among the exceptions.

There are three unresolved issues with respect to such agricultural research centers in poor countries: (1) the number, (2) the competence of the scientific personnel, and (3) the optimum size. No doubt there are some small countries, like many of our financially poor states, that cannot afford even one first-rate center. But what about countries as vast and diverse as Brazil and India?[6] Here, again, our own experiences are most telling. It would have been absurd to opt for only one such center in the United States and to locate it outside Washington, D.C. It is fully as absurd to conceive of Pusa at New Delhi as the agricultural research center for all of India. As to the second issue, clearly there is no substitute for scientific competence. The AID-university contracts in general have not succeeded on this score. On the other hand the International Rice Research Institute in the Philippines is acquiring a highly competent staff, as has the agricultural research establishment in Mexico. On the matter of the optimum size of such centers, all too little is known. No one to my knowledge has examined the complementarity among scientists with a view of resolving this issue. A lone scientist is absurd; a small core may be far less than optimum. Our own experiences seem to support two inferences: (1) research scientists should be an integral part of a college or university, and (2) a number of competent persons no larger than that of most of our state agricultural experiment stations is inadequate. It may well be true that by this test less than ten of the agricultural research centers in the United States are of optimum size.

As to the second part of the foundation, that is, a supply of the high payoff agricultural inputs that farmers can acquire, once such inputs have been discovered, developed, and tested, who will produce and supply them to farmers? The multiplication and distribution of new seeds is an example. In general this is not the kind of activity that experiment stations and extension services can carry on efficiently. Nor can this task be efficiently performed by a ministry of agriculture or cooperatives that do not operate for profit. Ways and means must be found to transfer these activities to firms that operate for profit. Needless to say, many of the governments in poor countries either distrust such private profit-making firms or seek to build little empires for themselves within the public domain, and they therefore prefer not to transfer these essential supply functions to firms that are subject to the discipline of the market.

The third part of the foundation requires that farmers be provided information about these inputs and learn how to use them. In a strict sense, this can be undertaken only after the other two parts are ready. Thus, there is a kind of natural order, a basic sequence in what can be done to modernize agriculture. But we have repeatedly made the mistake of undertaking the last part before the other two were in place. In Peru, for example, by the early 1950's a remarkably fine agricultural extension service had been developed, but unfortunately it ran dry because the supply of rewarding agricultural inputs was inadequate. In my judgment this also is the situation in India. Moreover, our experiences in the United States should have taught us this lesson. Our state agricultural extension services during the early years appear to have had little worthwhile information for farmers. The many efforts that we made during World War I to expand agricultural production and the lack of success of these efforts support this inference. Agricultural production in the United States during 1917-19 was only a scant 1 percent more than it had been during 1912-14.[7] Where the aim is economic growth from agriculture, there is no escaping the fact that unless there is a supply of rewarding inputs that farmers can acquire, an agricultural extension service is an empty institutional gesture.

But the right time for extension work is only one of the facets of information and learning which are under consideration. The costs to farmers are another facet. These costs depend among other things on the complexity of the new production process facing farmers. In considering costs there is a basic proposition with respect to the rate at which farmers will accept a new agricultural input. It is here proposed as an hypothesis: *The rate of acceptance depends predominantly on the profitability of the new input.* Unquestionably, the greater the complexity of the new process the larger these costs. Suppose there is a new highly profitable variety which requires only a few simple changes in traditional farm practices. In this case the costs to farmers of acquiring the information and of learning its use are small, and it follows that an elaborate extension program would be superfluous. Some new inputs are so profitable that as they become available farmers swamp the suppliers with their demands for them. Though such inputs, like striking a gushing oil well, are not frequent, in launching agricultural programs abroad there is much to be said for finding and developing precisely this class of inputs. Drawing on our own experience, hybrid corn was such a discovery, and as a consequence, farmers in the heart of the corn belt—where hybrid corn proved to be most rewarding—adopted the hybrid seed rapidly in spite of the very low corn prices that prevailed during the early and middle 1930's.

As the modernizing of agriculture proceeds, however, farming becomes increasingly complex. Many new inputs become profitable only after a multiplicity of changes in practices which require much information and learning on the part of farmers.

Still another facet of this type of information and learning is the complementarity between the activities of firms for profit, chiefly the suppliers of new inputs, and nonmarket agencies such as the extension services and schools. This facet is often overlooked in our activities abroad, despite our success in this respect in the United States. I have dealt with this complementarity elsewhere.[8]

There is one more facet of information and learning that I shall only mention, although it may well be the most important of them all. Taking the long view, it is essential to see that the acquisition of new skills by farm people is also one of the primary new profitable inputs. Though I have concentrated on new material inputs and though they are necessary to a limited extent, the fruit from the advance in knowledge that is useful in economic endeavors is to an even larger extent dependent upon new skills. The necessity of learning the skills that are required for modernizing agriculture brings up the issue of investing in farm people.[9] How to do this most efficiently is a matter about which we know all too little as yet. Crash programs are warranted under some circumstances. So are demonstrations designed to instruct farmers. There is also a place for some on-the-job training. But investment in schooling is in all probability the most economical way when one takes a ten- to twenty-year view of the process. What this means is that the rate of return to the costs of schooling, especially at the primary level, is probably exceedingly high, higher than the return to the investment in any of the alternative ways of acquiring these new skills.

Anthony M. Tang's[10] recent study of inputs and the output of Japanese agriculture permits me to close with an exceedingly encouraging estimate of the rate of return to investment in agricultural research, extension, and schooling. This estimate is for the period from 1880 to 1938. During the first five years of this period fully 98 percent of the total outlays for these purposes was for schooling. At the end of the period, that is, in the last five years, schooling was still 91 percent and agricultural research and extension about 9 percent of the total outlays. The social rate of return to all of this schooling, research, and extension was a handsome 35 percent a year. Where could one do better than this in achieving economic growth?

IV

Modern Agriculture

Millet's pictures of the European peasant of his day
tell us more about traditional agriculture than the
poet's idyllic imagery of farm life. Neither artist,
however, has given us insights into modern agriculture. Grant Wood's "American Gothic" is no exception. It is still too soon to reckon fully the economic
implications of modern agriculture. But when it can
be done with the perspective of history, I am sure it
will show that it is one of the really important sources
of economic growth.

While waiting for the historian, one might look for
a moment upon modern agriculture as a young lady
of many talents and moods. She is obviously very in-
fluential politically. When courted by government
her tastes are expensive, but she cannot be won by
force, as is clear from the Soviet experience. She is
unabashed in giving her favors to the consumers of
food yet heartless in her treatment of her own people
—in the stresses and strains she imposes on many
farm people. There are those who think of modern
agriculture as fickle in her economic affairs, but they
are wrong, for she is shrewdly calculating in these
matters. Nor should we overlook her most important

talent, that of dispelling the age-old anxiety concerning food.

From an economist's view of modern agriculture, I shall consider the following questions:

1. What are the sources of the gains in agricultural productivity in the United States?

2. Why has the Soviet Union been unable to develop these sources of productivity?

3. Is there a basis for redistributing the "losses" borne by farm people as a consequence of these gains in productivity?

4. Why do farm people fail to share in many of the social services of our welfare state?

PRODUCTIVITY

The gains in agricultural productivity not only here but also in Western Europe, Israel, Japan, and Mexico are indeed remarkable. I shall, however, restrict my comments to the United States for two reasons: (1) the increases began here, and (2) recent studies identify the sources.

To see that the increases have been impressively large, one need only look at output in relation to land and labor. Since 1945 crop production has risen 45 percent an acre and farm output per man-hour has almost tripled. Total farm output rose nearly two-fifths,[1] although cropland harvested declined by 54,000,000 acres—down 15 percent. The land thus released since 1945 is equal in area to the combined cropland harvested in Michigan, Ohio, Indiana, and Iowa, with 3,000,000 acres to spare.[2] Yet by comparison, that labor in farming is down by more than half seems incredible. At the close of World War II to have predicted that by 1964 it would be reduced by one-half would have been baseless fancy. Meanwhile, farming is no longer predominantly hard manual work. The level of skills has risen, the hours of work have declined about as rapidly as in industry, and the productivity of labor in agriculture has been rising two to three times as fast as in industry. By comparison industry is really backward!

Since the recent increases in agricultural production in India are readily explained and since those in the United States are not, it may be helpful to re-examine both of them. It has required about 25 percent more inputs to obtain 25 percent more output in India since 1945.[3] The labor force in agriculture increased over a fourth, which induced complementary investment in material things, for example, 29 percent more bullocks, 42 percent more carts, and 33 percent more irrigation—altogether about one-third more reproducible material capital.[4] Land, of course, did not increase as much, yet the area sown rose a tenth partly because of more double cropping. Also the large investment in irrigation added to the effective capacity of land. All of these inputs were of the traditional type, predominantly from within agriculture, and the ratio of these inputs to agricultural output remained virtually constant. Meanwhile, in sharp contrast, agricultural production in the United States rose 38 percent while total inputs, as these are officially measured, rose only 3 percent.[5] Thus, we have an unexplained divergency of 35 percentage points, that is, output up 38 percent minus the rise in inputs of only 3 percent.

It is noteworthy that during the first quarter of this century the growth of agriculture in the United States behaved much like that in India. Ruttan's[6] estimates for 1900 to 1925, already referred to, show inputs increasing 1.0 percent a year with output rising only 0.9 of 1 percent. Accordingly, this was a period not only of slow agricultural growth but one during which the rise in inputs exceeded slightly that of output. There is much that is puzzling about this period. Why didn't U.S. agriculture perform better? Was it because of a lack of an advance in knowledge from research despite the fact that the Hatch Act had been providing federal funds to the state agricultural experiment stations since 1887? Agriculture extension work had also become widely established, and many measures were undertaken during World War I to increase agricultural production. Nor were incentives lacking, for prices rose, and the prices of farm products increased relative to wholesale prices generally. Yet despite all of this, agricultural output grew slowly, while the annual rate of increase of inputs exceeded that of outputs.

This situation changes dramatically soon after 1925, as output climbs and exceeds inputs. Here, then we enter upon the recent period already described. But the sources of these remarkable gains in productivity have been most elusive. It is ever so convenient to say the ratio of output to inputs has risen. Yet such a rise in productivity has come from somewhere. To attribute it to technology is an empty gesture, a sleight of hand at which economists are all too adept, but it only conceals their ignorance. The fact is that any change in technology always requires a change in inputs.[7] The answer is to be found in three interrelated developments.

1. *Advance in knowledge.* The agricultural research establishment has discovered and developed many new things, based on the advance in knowledge, that are useful and profitable in agricultural production. One set consists of material things which have come from biology, chemistry, physics, and mechanics. Here the advance in knowledge becomes an integral part of some material inputs, for example, knowledge with respect to hybridization becomes a part of hybrid corn. The other set consists of practices in the art of farming acquired by farmers. Here the advance in knowledge becomes an integral part of what human beings know and practice, for example, knowing the optimum combination of fertilizers for particular soils and of feed nutrients for the different farm animals.

2. *Supply of new material inputs.* The suppliers of these inputs are predominantly private firms for profit. Farmers in general purchase these inputs from the nonfarm sectors as machines, tractors, fertilizer, pesticides, insecticides, and also genetically superior seeds, plants, and animals. Inputs of "higher quality" have thus become available to farmers. Moreover, the supply price of some of them has been declining; notable and important in this respect is the marked decline in the price of fertilizer relative to farm product prices.[8]

3. *The advance in farmers' know-how.* The advance in knowledge has neither simplified nor routinized farming. The amount of manual work has declined, but the skill required has risen. Farmers have responded by improving their abilities as producers. These acquired abilities can be traced back to new information made available to them by the press and related media and by the agricultural extension service. But most of the advance in this area has come from schooling, namely, from the completion of more years of school and from schooling of higher quality than formerly.

Thus, the first of these developments—the advance in knowledge—sets the stage for the other two. There is also a complicated process of *acceptance, adoption,* and *adjustment.* How much is known about the production effects of these developments? There is a lively intellectual interest of some years' standing in economics at The University of Chicago in two key questions: (1) Is it possible to specify and identify these sources of productivity gains? (2) How high is the rate of return to research, extension activities, and schooling?

The pioneer work of my colleague Zvi Griliches begins with his study of hybrid corn. He found that the cumulated past research expenditures, private and public, as of 1955, came to $131,000,000 on which for each dollar the social returns came to at least $7.00 annually, or a 700 percent rate of return.[9] He then devised methods to estimate the improvements in the quality of farm machinery, concentrating on farm tractors, and of the farm labor force, by taking schooling into account. His most recent work, which also includes a correction for "scale effects," successfully accounts for "all" of the sources of the measured productivity growth of agriculture in the United States between 1940 and 1960.[10] The rate of return to fertilizer has been exceedingly high, but it has been declining, for farmers have been responding. Schooling of farmers and of others who work at farming proves to be an important source. My estimates of over a decade ago of the high payoff on agricultural research are being confirmed.

<h3 style="text-align:center">SOVIET PLIGHT</h3>

The now disposed of Mr. Khrushchev told a factory audience in Budapest, "The important thing is we should have more to eat good goulash." Every Russian family would agree. He was aware that the ballet is good but agriculture is bad. Moreover, he was haunted by what he saw of Iowa farms some years ago. Upon his return he launched a vigorous program to produce more corn to produce more meat to make better goulash. But despite all of Mr. Khrushchev's agricultural experience and all his grand plans to produce more food, the record speaks for itself. Since none of the Soviet-type economies has been able to develop a highly productive agriculture, the question is, why?

I noted in Chapter I that the reason for this failure is not that Russia does not have scientists; it has to its credit a long tradition of science applied to agriculture, and the government has generously supported the agricultural research establishment. New machinery, especially big tractors, has been vigorously promoted. But all this has been of little avail. Now new massive programs are to be undertaken to increase the amount and use of fertilizer and to enlarge the area under irrigation.[11] But will these be any more successful than the big tractors, the new lands, and the hybrid corn? The odds are that they will not.

Bad crop years aside, additional investment in irrigation and fertilizer with still more mechanization and specialization and the appointment and promotion of better agricultural planners and administrators will no doubt increase Soviet agricultural production. But these measures will not be sufficient to achieve the growth in productivity that can be had from modern agriculture, as is clear in the case of Czechoslovakia, which has been investing heavily in agriculture, including fertilizer, and yet agriculture has done badly.[12] A comparison between Czechoslovakia and Western Europe shows that from 1934-38 to 1956, farm tractors increased over eightfold in Czechoslovakia, almost as much as in Western Europe; imported feed rose more than fourfold, fully twice that in Western Europe; and fertilizers also rose fourfold, while in Western Europe they did not quite double. But agricultural output in Czechoslovakia was not as large in 1956 as it had been during 1934-38, whereas in Western Europe it had already risen 25 percent by 1956,[13] and it has increased another 25 percent since then, while in Czechoslovakia it has hardly increased at all.

What is lacking in agriculture in all Soviet-type economies is by now altogether obvious. The lack is not science or "technology," or machinery including tractors, or irrigation, or fertilizer. What is lacking is a system of economic incentives that will permit and induce farm people to modernize agriculture. State control which entails absentee production decisions—no matter how frequently the control apparatus is reorganized, how many different approaches are tried, and how competent the administrators—will continue to be inefficient. To modernize requires the acceptance and adoption by farmers of many new agricultural inputs, and it also requires that farmers learn how to use these inputs efficiently. Thus, resident decisions by operating farmers, responding to meaningful economic incentives, are indispensable. Until the Soviet Union develops such a system of economic incentives, there simply will not be enough "good goulash."

LOSSES IN FARM INCOME FROM PRODUCTIVITY GROWTH

For many farm people modern agriculture is no bed of roses. The impressive production statistics of agriculture in the United States do not bring prosperity to farmers. The very success of modern agriculture, as a producing sector, places many farm people under severe economic stresses. The growth in productivity has required all manner of adjustments. But the term "adjustment" fails to convey the hard economic facts and the trouble farmers are in. The farm population of the United States has been cut in half since 1943; back of this harsh fact is the unprecedented mass migration of people who have left agriculture in the hope of improving their economic lot. Yet there are still all too many people trying to earn their living at farming, and as a consequence many of them earn relatively little.

In terms of public policy we have done badly in coping with this situation. Since the legislative intent of our agricultural price and production programs has not been to correct the economic imbalance burdening agriculture, no wonder, then, that these programs have failed to meet the resource allocative test. More specifically, they have failed to assist farm people who want to leave agriculture and who ought to leave it in view of economic considerations. They have failed to help these people find nonfarm jobs, prepare for such jobs, and migrate to where they are to be had. Instead, they have induced overinvestment in material inputs, including a serious overvaluation of farm land. The economic function of farm product prices has been impaired substantially; agricultural production has been subsidized, which has led to considerable dumping of U.S. farm products abroad. Nor has the intent of public policy been to transfer income to farm people based on welfare standards. In terms of welfare services farm people have come off badly relative to urban people.

With this as a preface, the unsettled issue of how the gains and losses from productivity growth should be distributed can be considered.[14] The rules of the economic game are that these particular gains and losses are to be absorbed by labor (including management) and by those who own the material resources as changes in demands and supplies reveal themselves in their respective markets. The rationale of this policy rests on the belief that economic progress entails all manner of demand and supply changes. There is the belief that the relevant changes are not only numerous but that they also take many unanticipated turns and twists and, thus, planning and policy to cope with them are not possible. A further belief is that these changes occur slowly and gradually, that they are widely diffused, and that the resulting windfall gains and losses are not accumulative in the way they come to rest on the particular workers and resource owners. Lastly, and of great importance, is the strongly held belief that these particular gains and losses are the essential inducements to get labor and owners of resources to make the necessary adjustments called for by economic progress. Thus, it should surprise no one that it has long been held that it is the better part of wisdom to let the chips fall where they may. In line with that wisdom, we have evolved our traditional policy which *lets* and which *requires* labor and those who own the nonhuman resources to absorb the windfall gains and the "unforeseen" losses that occur as a consequence of economic progress.

How well grounded are the beliefs about economic progress on which our traditional policy rests? Are the gains and losses from economic progress widely distributed? Among consumers, yes. But not so among producers. What this means is that consumers gain qua consumers, although some of them lose in their capacity as producers. For example, a decline in real costs in producing farm products as a consequence of economic progress soon benefits all consumers, including farm people purely in their capacity as consumers, but some farm people can lose more as producers than they gain as consumers from this process.

Producer gains and losses from economic progress are by no means evenly distributed. For example, there are the losses as revealed in what are called "depressed areas." Areas dependent on coal mining and, in New England, on textiles have long been depressed. Other industrial activities also leave entire communities seriously depressed as a consequence of supply and demand changes arising from economic progress. Much of our agriculture, because of the rapid rate of improvements in the production possibilities in farming, because of the slow rate at which the demand schedule for farm products shifts to the right, and because of difficulties in adjusting to these changes, becomes depressed. No one can any longer maintain that these producer losses from economic progress are distributed at all evenly among *occupations, industries,* and *areas.*

Moreover, many of these producer losses from economic progress are accumulative, that is, they continue to mount and to burden particular occupations, industries, and areas, over long periods of time. Northern textiles, coal mining, and agriculture have been up against such losses from economic progress for many decades. The end is not in sight for agriculture.

There is also the belief that none of these producer losses can be dealt with by policy and by appropriate public measures because none of them can be foreseen. They are thought to be in the realm of the unknown—losses that occur as a result of pure uncertainty. Here, again, the evidence does not support such an extreme position. Particular classes of people, such as workers and even some owners of nonhuman resources, are absorbing such losses not because *no one knew* that the losses would occur but because some people are caught in a process from which they find it exceedingly hard to extricate themselves. Older farm people are thus caught. The "salvage" value of their skills, if they were to leave agriculture, is even less than the reduced earnings they can win for themselves in farming. The quasi rent on what they have invested in skills and knowledge in order to farm falls because even though younger people leave agriculture there is a long lag. There is always a transfer price which has the characteristics of a human investment. Why do younger people leave agriculture more readily than do older people? The reason for this selective migration by age may simply rise out of the fact that the costs of migrating and of acquiring new skills represent a substantial investment; for older people there are not enough years remaining to warrant making such an investment in themselves. Thus, they stay and absorb the loss although they are aware of it.

It is well known that much of agriculture will

sustain losses that are a consequence of economic progress for years to come. The rub here is not that there is no relevant knowledge but that some farm people cannot act on it in ways to escape serious losses for themselves.

As to the belief that any attempt to redistribute these producer losses from economic progress will inevitably undermine and ultimately destroy our open market economy, in the proposal that follows the essence of the incentive system will be preserved by giving free rein to the windfall gains from economic progress. This means that these gains will have to carry a larger load, in fact the entire burden of inducing people to make the necessary adjustments called for by economic progress. But this is not the whole of the story, for the present distribution of these losses in many situations gives rise to a kind of reverse English, because they undermine the capital and credit position of workers and of the owners of the nonhuman resources who absorb the losses and because once caught in such a situation, no small amount of capital is frequently required to extricate oneself.

In the case of agriculture, weight must also be given to the fact that some of these producer losses from economic progress falling on farm people are a consequence of public policy to support agricultural research and to disseminate the new knowledge from such research so that it will be adopted rapidly and effectively. The new and better production possibilities that have characterized our agriculture and that are continuing in farming are in no small part a consequence of such public programs.

An alternative policy and the reasons in support of it will now be presented. Ideally, the objective of this policy is to ensure individuals from losses caused by economic progress. How to identify these losses and how to protect individuals against them are no doubt important, practical matters. Before turning to them, however, I want to consider what such a policy will do to incentives in general. It would redistribute the losses, but it would not alter directly the windfall gains from economic progress that labor and owners of nonhuman resources now absorb. These gains, accordingly, are not to be captured (indirectly they will be modified). It is of critical importance not to take away these gains because they become the incentives to induce labor and resource owners to make the required adjustments. It is assumed that these losses are much smaller than the gains and, therefore, that the net aggregate gains from economic progress are not only large but large enough to provide an effective system of incentives. These incentives are an essential part of this policy because they make possible the maintenance of the substance of an open economy.

What is the basis for distinguishing between losses from economic progress and all of the other losses that occur? What are the forms of compensation that are efficient in achieving the objective of this policy? Is it feasible for a government to administer such compensation? These are difficult questions, but they are no more formidable than those that arose in our efforts to cope with mass unemployment.

The losses from mass unemployment are an instructive analogue. We do well to remember that there were many serious objections to any policy whatsoever to deal with mass unemployment. Many people, lay and professional, firmly believed that any public measures to treat this unemployment would seriously impair the economy; now, too, there are many who look in the same way upon measures to deal with the losses from economic progress, as is clear from some of the objections to the "depressed areas" legislation. There are some who thought—in the case of mass unemployment—that public measures were unnecessary because if only wages were more flexible there would be no such unemployment. Similarly, there are those who believe that the resource malallocations caused by economic progress would rapidly correct themselves if only market prices were free and flexible.

Yet out of our trials and errors from what we have learned about booms and recessions, there is now a strong consensus that economic stability is an important objective to be achieved through public measures. There are, as we all know, still substantial disagreements about the appropriate fiscal, monetary, and other measures for achieving the objective of economic stability. There also are unemployment payments and these, too, are still far from satisfactory. The point is that the question concerning mass unemployment is no longer, "Should there be a policy to cope with it?" That question has been settled in favor of having such a policy. The question now is, "How can it be done more efficiently than is the case at present?" But we are not at this stage in dealing with the losses from economic progress. Neither our analytical work nor the public policy debate is addressed to the question of ways and means. The issue that is still before us is comparable to the first, namely, "Should there be a policy to cope with the losses from economic progress?" I have attempted to show that such a policy is warranted because of our kind of economic growth, because of the uneven way the losses from economic progress are distributed and the welfare implications of this unequal distribution of such losses, and because there is a logical basis for redistributing these losses through public measures.

In implementing this policy, there are good reasons for beginning with the losses borne by labor including the self-employed and management, and for leaving aside until later how best to treat the losses that owners of resources bear as a consequence of economic progress. First, we have a strong precedent for doing so in the early approach to mass unemployment: when unemployment insurance was undertaken, no "insurance" was provided for unemployed plants and equipment, although at a later stage tax laws were altered to enable firms to spread their losses. Second, the adjustments confronting labor are as a rule subject to longer lags than are those for nonhuman resources. Human beings have a much longer productive life than do most forms of reproducible physical capital. Thus, by doing no more than not replacing the machines and tractors that wear out, the stock is rapidly reduced over time, whereas people retire from the work they are doing only after four decades or more of work. Third, workers, because of compelling cultural reasons, are unique in producing not only their own replacement but for good measure add to their numbers. Imagine how different the farm problem would be if no farm children had been born during these last several decades! Also, in the case of agriculture, the human investment in skills and knowledge required to farm is very substantial, and the demand for these particular skills and this knowledge elsewhere in the economy is small. Lastly, there is the obvious fact that most members of the labor force are tied to families and are rooted in communities which they are reluctant to leave. We do well for these several reasons to concentrate on labor in treating the losses from economic progress.

I can do no more than mention the types of public measures that are likely to prove useful in achieving the objectives of this particular policy. Two broad lines of action are open to us: (1) measures to accelerate the adjustment process, and (2) measures to compensate those who nevertheless bear losses. (Note the parallelism, once again, to what has been done in dealing with mass unemployment: there have been various measures to reduce the fluctuations in business activities with a view of attaining economic stability and thus to achieve more nearly continuous full employment; there also have been

payments to cushion the losses in earnings from unemployment.)

To accelerate the adjustment process does not
mean that the goal is to eliminate the lag in this adjustment altogether, any more than the goal of economic stability is to eliminate all fluctuations in business. Even though it were possible to devise programs that would eliminate this lag, it would undoubtedly be all too costly to do so. What is implied,
however, is that the lag at present is all too long in
the sense that much could be gained from a reckon-
ing of costs and returns by reducing it substantially.[15]

WHY WELFARE SERVICES
FOR FARM PEOPLE ARE NEGLECTED[16]

Professor Jacob Viner acutely and correctly characterizes the style of organization of the American
economy as that of a *welfare state*. The welfare state
so conceived represents a partial rejection of laissez
faire as it prevailed fairly widely in the Western
world during the nineteenth century, when "the
emphasis was on freedom for the individual from
government, not on service to him by government."
It also rejects the modern form of the authoritarian
state in which, by abandoning political and civil
freedom, the emphasis is on service to the individual
determined from above and enforced by coercion.
Between these two systems there has emerged a welfare state which "tries to find a middle path between
service without freedom and freedom without service."[17]

Farmers in the United States have had a large hand politically in developing our welfare state, long before the New Deal and McNary-Haugenism. The earlier agrarian movements protested strongly against the doctrine of laissez faire not because farm leaders had been schooled in European socialism or in Marxian thought. Their protests were a direct, indigenous response to the raw industrialism of the post-Civil War decades and to the long decline in the general level of prices. In practice, laissez faire, so it seemed to many farm people, sheltered all manner of monopolies; the agrarian movements demanded that the trusts be busted, and they eventually saw the enactment of far-reaching antitrust legislation. They were also convinced that private banks with an eye to profits had all too free a hand in determining the supply of money, regardless of what it did to the economy and to farmers as debtors. Bryan electrified a political convention by espousing the agrarian cause in his "Cross of Gold." As a response, although after a long lag, the Federal Reserve System was established.[18] In retrospect it is noteworthy that these early farm leaders anticipated what has since become a major purpose of modern monetary-fiscal policy.[19] They also protested the then extreme inequalities in the distribution of personal income and wealth.[20] But for all these important modifications of the doctrine of laissez faire, farm people have not acquired for themselves many of the major social services of the welfare state.[21]

The anomaly is that there are important services now provided by our welfare state in which farm people have been reluctant to share. They generally are opposed to extending to hired farm labor the unemployment and related benefits available to non-farm laborers. There is virtually no concern on the part of farm people about the social deprivation of migratory farm workers or about the social costs of cheap imported farm labor. For years there appeared to be widespread uneasiness among farm people in having old-age and survivor insurance extended to farmers, although it has become in less than a decade a major source of benefits, more important in terms of welfare than much of the farm legislation enacted on behalf of agriculture.[22] Except for agricultural vocational training and for land-grant teaching, research, and extension work, there is strong opposition to any and all federal aid to education. The same is generally true with regard to public measures for medical care and health facilities.[23]

Is there less need? The reluctance of farm people to participate in these social services of the welfare state may simply mean that there is no need. Just what is meant by "need" here is hard to say. Is it a matter of already having such services, or of not wanting them? Equivalent social services might be supplied presumably by private endeavor, or the demand for them might be very weak.

It is probably true that farm families are still somewhat more closely knit personally than are urban families; thus for any given level of income and wealth they do more than urban families do for the aged and other family members who are in need. It is also cheaper, at least to the extent that there is something for them to do. Moreover, in terms of wealth the net asset position of farmers who are farming is impressively large, approximately $35,800 per farmer in 1963.[24] While there are $125 billion of net assets back of this average figure, it hides a vast amount of inequality in the personal distribution of wealth among farm families. But our statistics are bad when it comes to determining how many farm families are too poor to acquire even a minimum level of consumption including housing, health and recreational services, and education for their children compatible with our national income and values. We have long been complaisant about American poverty, saying we are the affluent society. Except for the highly controversial New Deal Farm Security Administration, United States farm policy and programs have been blind to the welfare needs of Negroes in agriculture. There are still many of them on farms and they are mostly very poor. The 1960 Census tells us that nearly 8 percent of all farm operators were non-white. In the South fully 16 percent of the farm operators were Negroes. While the value of farms operated in the South by whites averaged $25,400, quite low as compared to the rest of the United States, the value of farms operated by Negroes was only $6,200 per farm. In terms of median income, white farm families were three times as well off as nonwhite farm families. Farm males, ages 25 and over, had completed 8.7 (median) years of schooling as compared to only 4.8 years on the part of the non-white males, and in addition the *quality* of schooling of nonwhites was much inferior to that of whites.

School dropouts tell a similar story; the figures for farm males, 14 to 24 years of age, are 22 and 41 percent, respectively.

Without belaboring the matter further, the reluctance of farm people to participate in the social services of the United States is not because there is no need for such services, for, in addition to the low economic and social lot of American Indians, Mexican nationals, and Negroes on farms, there are also many other poor farm families. One sees their lot in what these families can afford to consume and how they live; one sees it in many rural farm communities in the low quality of schooling and of health facilities.

The United States welfare state contributes relatively few social services benefiting farm people. Why this should be true is the puzzle with which I began. It is evidently not for lack of need on the part of farm people. Nor is it because they are strongly committed to laissez faire. The Grange, Populists, and Non-Partisan League were all protest movements demanding that this doctrine be modified. The roots that fed these earlier protests are still very much alive. Nor is it because farm people hold that all property rights including farm property rights are inalienable, as is clear from the many legal restrictions that have been placed, in general with the consent of farm people, on the use of land in relation to grazing, erosion control, watershed protection, dam sites, and forestry and mineral rights. I doubt also that it is because farm people are substantially more concerned than other people about the presumed corrupting of the moral fiber to work and earn one's keep once the state becomes a large source of social services.[25]

As I interpret our political and economic history, there are four major reasons for the neglect by government of the social aspects of welfare of farm people.

Influence of the Southern Tradition

The South is a key, critical part of agriculture. It accounted for over 45 percent of all United States farms when the last agricultural census was taken in 1959. Jefferson's agricultural views are often featured. But what is not emphasized is the political influence of the *Southern Tradition,* long supported by an undemocratic political structure. The weakness of this tradition with respect to social responsibility is ever so evident in an indifference and antagonism to public schools. Professor W. H. Nicholls' study leaves no room for doubt on this matter.[26]

Conflicts of Interest

Who represents whom with respect to the interests of farm people? Or, more narrowly, which class of farmers is represented? Or, precisely, which particular interests of particular farmers? Although the conflicts among farm commodity groups are well known, they have little direct bearing on the welfare issues under consideration. What is relevant here is the conflict in interest between imported farm laborers and the farmers who want cheap labor. Migratory farm laborers of domestic origin are similarly situated, as are hired farm workers generally. There is also the long-standing animosity of the poor Southern whites toward Negroes. Another conflict exists when it comes to a national sharing of some of the costs of schooling with its implied tax burden on the North and West to assist the South, where taxes on farmland to support local schools are often far less relative to the value of farmland than in the rest of the country. Patently, the poorest whose needs are the greatest have had the least political influence which is necessary to gain access to the social services of our welfare state.

A Lack of Knowledge

Farm people and their leaders are not in general conversant with the ideas, the philosophical basis, and historical processes that are part and parcel of the urbanization and industrialization of which modern agriculture is an integral part. The scientific and technological knowledge underlying modern agriculture is well understood by farm people, but the changing social and economic framework is still largely in the realm of myth. Some blame must fall on our land-grant colleges and universities. Where are the county agents who can hold forth competently on these cultural, economic, and historical issues? But where is the instruction to prepare them for this task? Even today there are few instructors who understand modern monetary-fiscal analysis. In the area of cultural and historical analysis, research and instruction are a gaping void.

Price-Production   Programs

Programs, which hold top priority in United States farm policy, afford the principal reason for the neglect by government of the welfare of farm people. Virtually all of the time and thought of the United States Department of Agriculture, the agricultural committees of Congress, and the farm organizations is spent on them. They exhaust the political influence of farm people. But these programs do not improve the schooling of farm children, they do not reduce the inequalities in personal distribution of wealth and income, they do not remove the cause of poverty in agriculture, nor do they alleviate it. On the contrary they worsen the personal distribution of income within agriculture.

But is this summary of their income effects not a flat contradiction of what really happens? Surely, it will be said, high price supports, with or without large government payments, must mean that farm income is larger than it would otherwise be, which in turn means that farm people can afford the consumption underlying welfare. Faith in this false proposition has lasted unbelievably long. Ever since the McNary-Haugen period, parity prices, parity income, acreage allotments, government payments, and then an expensive round of supply management, have held the center of the farm policy stage. Who benefits most? Landowners. Who least? The poorest farm families. By any meaningful welfare test, this is absurd.

There are some signs that some farm people have

lost faith in these production-price programs. Nevertheless, alternative programs designed to reduce the real poverty in agriculture, to raise the level of consumption of those who are very poor, and to provide first-class primary and secondary schooling for farm children are not welcomed by the agricultural committees of Congress or demanded politically by the strongest representatives of farm people. The belief is still strong that there must be some way of putting a bell on the cat by tying farm welfare to the production-price programs.

No doubt a system of forward prices, provided they are set with an eye to clearing the market, as in soybeans, could enhance the efficiency of agriculture and protect farmers against major fluctuations in the prices of what they sell. Programs to assist farmers to shift marginal crop land into long-term other uses are also required. But even well-conceived programs of this type will not resolve the need for social services by farm people.

But four high walls keep these social services from farm people: The political influence of the *Southern Tradition*, the conflict among farm people, the state of ideas of farm leaders, and their vested interest in production-price programs. But even these formidable walls will come tumbling down.

My aim has been to clarify the basic economic choices. I find that in most of the world farmers have long since exhausted the profitability of the state of the arts at their disposal. Their lot is that of traditional agriculture. The policy choice that matters here is investment in man and in things that will raise the level of the state of the arts. In modern agriculture the choice is more complex. There is still a serious underinvestment in farm people. The losses borne by farm people as a consequence of their productivity gains can and should be reduced and those that remain can and should be redistributed. The welfare services provided by government—among which schooling is very important—should be extended to farm people in equal measure to those now extended to nonfarm people.

Notes

CHAPTER I

1. See my "Value of U.S. Farm Surpluses to Under-developed Countries," *Journal of Farm Economics,* 42 (December 1960); and Franklin M. Fisher, "Agricultural Production in Recipient Countries," *Journal of Farm Economics,* 45 (November 1963). It is not that the P.L. 480 imports are lacking in value to the recipient country; the rub is their probable adverse effects on internal farm prices. These can be averted if proper means are taken and the country has the administrative capacity to promulgate these measures.

2. For a broad sketch of these in terms of unresolved problems see my *Transforming Traditional Agriculture,* Chapter 1, "The Problem and Its Setting" (New Haven: Yale University Press, 1964).

3. Based on Supplements of *The 1963 World Agricultural Situation,* Econ. Res. Service, U.S.D.A. While I have selected Japan because of the importance of increasing food production in Asia, the success of Mexico and Israel also belongs here. Both of these countries appear to have tripled their agricultural production since 1935-39.

4. Lester R. Brown, *Food Consumption and Expenditures: India, Japan, United States,* Foreign Agric.

Econ. Report Number 42 (U.S.D.A., 1962), Table 2.

5. *Ibid.*, Table 3, also see Table 4.

6. H. S. Houthakker in a "Discussion," *Journal of Farm Economics*, 45 (1963), 351-54, in commenting on W. W. Wilcox's paper, "The Rationality of United States Agricultural Policies," had this to say: "More dangerous, perhaps, is another argument that has recently become quite prominent in official propaganda. This is the argument from the diminishing share of food in consumers' expenditure, which Wilcox and others count as one of the blessings of agriculture. In fact, it is simply a consequence of Engel's law. Americans spend a smaller proportion of their income on food than people elsewhere not because American food prices are so low (they are not) but because their incomes are so high. These high incomes are due only to a small extent to the high productivity of American farms. The neglect of demand factors revealed here and elsewhere in Wilcox's paper is typical of a major flaw in the 'official view,' namely, its failure to see agriculture in perspective as a component of the general economy" (quoted with the author's permission).

7. For a summary of the very useful estimates made by L. M. Goreux, see *Agricultural Commodities Projections for 1970*, FAO Commodity Review, 1962, Special Supplement (Rome: FAO, 1962), Table M-4.

8. National Council of Applied Economic Research, *Long Term Projections of Demand and Supply of Selected Agricultural Commodities 1960–61 to 1975–76* (New Delhi, India, 1962). Table A-47 shows 290,000,000 acres under crops in 1940–41 and 372,000,000 acres in 1958-59, gross area in both cases. *The Economic Report of the President*, 1963 (Washing-

ton, D.C.), Table C-75, shows that 362,000,000 acres of crops were harvested in 1944 and only 295,000,000 in 1962.

9. Fred L. Garlock and associates, *The Balance Sheet of Agriculture, 1962*, Agric. Inf. Bull. No. 270, U.S.D.A. (1962), Table 2. These measures of the stock of reproducible farm capital are based on official estimates. Since they do not reckon satisfactorily the improvements in the quality of such capital over time, they should be interpreted with this limitation in mind.

10. Tara Shukla, "Capital Formation in Agriculture in India, 1920–21 to 1960–61" (unpublished Ph.D. thesis, Department of Economics, University of Bombay, 1963), Table V-1. The index of the stock of durable physical capital in agriculture in India, excluding houses and land, rose from 92 in 1940–41 to 127 in 1960–61, an increase of 38 percent. Appendix 1-A shows that irrigation rose from 100 to 136, bullocks from 87 to 115, carts from 83 to 121, wooden ploughs from 82 to 120, and iron ploughs from 38 to 223—all with 1950–51 = 100.

11. Yet the per capita agricultural production of the rural population is more than twice as large in Japan as in Thailand.

12. See Tables 101 and 102 *Production Yearbook 1962* (Rome: FAO), Vol. 16. Most of these tractors are appropriately classified as garden-type tractors.

13. See Chapter 4, "The Doctrine of Agricultural Labor of Zero Value," in my *Transforming Traditional Agriculture*.

CHAPTER II

1. Thorkild Jacobsen, "Ancient Mesopotamian Religion: The Central Concerns," *Proceedings of the American*

Philosophical Society, 107, No. 6 (December 20, 1963).

2. From Psalms 127 and 78.
3. Homewood, Ill.: Dorsey Press, 1962. See the critical review by David C. McClelland, the psychologist, of Professor Hagen's book, "A Psychological Approach to Economic Development," *Economic Development and Cultural Change,* 12 (April 1964), 320–24.
4. Yale University Press, 1964.
5. First published by The Smithsonian Institute of Social Anthropology, Publication No. 16 (U.S. Government Printing Office, 1953). Reprinted by the University of Chicago Press, 1963.
6. An unpublished Ph.D. dissertation (Cornell University, 1957) under the title "The Economic Organization of a Village in North Central India."
7. Stanford University Press, 1964.
8. For example, Clifford Geertz in his very useful book *Agricultural Involution, the Process of Ecological Change in Indonesia* (Berkeley: University of California Press, 1963) is at times entangled in economic concepts which have led him to draw invalid economic inferences.
9. David Hume, *Writings on Economics* (Madison: University of Wisconsin Press, 1955), edited by Eugene Rotwein, p. 10. I am indebted to Mr. Nathan Rosenberg's paper, "Neglected Dimensions in the Analysis of Economic Change," for this and the following reference to Hume.
10. Hume, *op. cit.,* p. 50.
11. W. Arthur Lewis, *The Theory of Economic Growth* (London: George Allen and Unwin, 1955). See his index on "Work, attitude to" for page references.
12. *Ibid.,* p. 227.

13. "At the end of 1960 there were 44,000 collective farms
with, on the average, a sown area of 2745 hectares
and a total area of 6300 hectares; 7375 *sovkhozy* with
an average sown area of 9000 and a total area of
26,000 hectares . . . about 17 million private plots of
collective farm members with an average sown area
of less than 0.3 hectares; and about 18 million plots
of state employees living both in rural and urban
areas, the average size of each being about 0.10
hectares. Thus, Soviet agriculture consists of farm
sizes at the two extremes for the world: a fairly small
number of giant farms control about 94 percent of
the sown area, and perhaps 30 million tiny farm units
have only three percent of the sown area (in 1960
the total sown area of the private plots was 6,730,000
hectares). The tiny private plots, where the spade
and the hoe are the principal tools, produce a major
fraction of the total output and utilize a significant
share of the total labor input." From D. Gale Johnson, "Soviet Agriculture," *Bulletin of the Atomic
Scientists,* January, 1964, pp. 8–12.

14. Wllliam H. Nicholls, *Southern Tradition and Regional
Progress* (Chapel Hill: University of North Carolina
Press, 1960).

15. See my *Transforming Traditional Agriculture*, Chapter 8.

16. See *ibid.*, Chapter 4.

17. W. David Hopper, *op. cit.*, p. 161.

18. For a list of some of those who have sung this refrain,
see those listed in footnote 3 of Raj Krishna's, "Farm
Supply Response in India-Pakistan: A Case Study
of the Punjab Region," *The Economic Journal,* 73
(September 1963). Others who have been charmed
by this refrain are D. R. Khatkhate, "Some Notes on

the Real Effects of Foreign Surplus Disposal in Underdeveloped Areas," *Quarterly Journal of Economics,* 74 (May 1962); Joseph Grunwald, "The Structuratist School on Price Stability and Development," in *Latin American Issues,* ed. by A. O. Hirschman (New York: Twentieth Century Fund, 1961); and Kusum Nair, *Blossoms in the Dust* (London: Duckworth, 1961).

19. Lester R. Brown, *Agricultural Diversification and Economic Development in Thailand,* Foreign Agric. Econ. Report No. 8, U.S.D.A. (March 1963). A small boom has also been underway in Thailand in kenaf and cassava (see pp. 10–11).

20. *Ibid.,* p. 9. Corn yields were only 10 bushels per acre in 1950. By 1961 they had been increased to 25 bushels.

21. Based on an analysis by A. R. Abdel-Wahab while a graduate student at the University of Chicago. Data are from Annual Foreign Trade Report and Selected Internal Statistics, Department of Statistics, Khartoum, Sudan.

22. The profitability of sugarcane over that of paddy rice because of the high price for sugarcane guaranteed by the government and low controlled price for rice is ever so evident in a recent case study of farmers in eastern Uttar Pradesh, India, by S. C. Gupta and A. Majid, *Farmers' Response to Prices and Marketing Policies Affecting Sugarcane and Paddy,* Agricultural Economic Research Centre (University of Delhi, 1962). Reading this study, one feels that the authors tried hard to conjure all manner of explanatory factors for the shifts from paddy to sugarcane to obscure the obvious effects of the change in relative prices so favorable to producing sugarcane.

23. L. S. Venkataramanan, "A Statistical Study of Indian Jute Production and Marketing with Special Reference to Foreign Demand" (unpublished Ph.D. dissertation, University of Chicago, June 1958).
24. Raj Krishna, "Farm Supply Response in the Punjab: A Case Study of Cotton" (unpublished Ph.D. dissertation, University of Chicago, September 1961); and recent paper based on additional research, "Farm Supply Response in India-Pakistan: A Case Study of the Punjab Region," *The Economic Journal*, 73 (September 1963).
25. *Ibid.*, p. 486.
26. Walter P. Falcon, "Farmer Response to Price in an Underdeveloped Area: A Case Study of West Pakistan" (unpublished Ph.D. dissertation, Harvard University, 1962). Also "Farmer Response to Price in a Subsistence Economy: The Case of West Pakistan," read at the American Economic Association meetings, Boston, December 29, 1963.
27. Raj Krishna, *op. cit.*, p. 487.
28. Sol Tax, *op. cit.*
29. For a careful examination of Tax's data with respect to this issue, see my *Transforming Traditional Agriculture*, Chapter 3.
30. Dr. Hopper undertook this test of his data while he was a member of the faculty of economics at The University of Chicago. See Chapter 3 of *Transforming Traditional Agriculture*.
31. Once again I refer to *Transforming Traditional Agriculture*, Chapter 4. A new study is now at hand. Yong Sam Cho, *"Disguised Unemployment" in Underdeveloped Areas with Special Reference to South Korean Agriculture* (Berkeley and Los Angeles: University of California Press, 1963).

32. Analytically, I prefer, for reasons set forth in Chapter 5 of *Transforming Traditional Agriculture*, the concept of the price of the source of income streams, i.e., the reciprocal $\frac{1}{r}$ where r is the rate of return. A 10 percent rate thus implies a $10 price for a $1.00 per year income stream. To abstract from risk and uncertainty, it is for some purposes convenient to use the concept of a permanent income stream.

33. Here I am indebted to W. H. Nicholls and Ruy Miller Paiva for discussing with me the preliminary inferences from their field survey in this area.

34. *Transforming Traditional Agriculture*, p. 93.

35. *Ibid.*, p. 96.

CHAPTER III

1. This chapter is drawn substantially from my address to the American Association for the Advancement of Science at Cleveland, Ohio, December 30, 1963. It appears in *Agricultural Sciences for the Developing Nations*, Symposium proceedings published by the AAAS (Washington, D.C., 1964), and is reproduced here by permission of the Association.

2. In India the price of sugarcane and apparently also of potatoes relative to the price of fertilizer has been attractive to farmers, judging from their recent production behavior.

3. See *Technical Cooperation in Latin America*, National Planning Association (Washington, D.C., 1950). These studies were sponsored by the NPA. Several books based on these studies were published. They are listed in this report.

4. Martin L. Mosher, *Early Iowa Corn Yield Tests and*

Related Programs (Ames: Iowa State University Press, 1962).

5. Vernon W. Ruttan, "Technological Change and Resource Utilization in American Agriculture," *Proceedings of the Indiana Academy of Science for 1961,* 71 (1961), 353–60. Between 1925 and 1950, agricultural output rose at a rate of 1.5 percent per year while conventional inputs rose at a rate of only 0.4 percent per year.

6. We do well to remember that we, too, were relatively poor at the time we established the land-grant colleges. The Morrill Act came in 1862 when our real per capita GNP was about one-seventh of what it is now; and the Hatch Act providing federal funds for agricultural research came in 1887 when we were at one-fourth of the present per capita GNP level.

7. See Neal Potter and Francis T. Christy, Jr., *Trends in Natural Resource Commodities* (Baltimore: Johns Hopkins Press, 1962), Table EO-1, p. 81.

8. See Chapters 10 and 11 of my *Transforming Traditional Agriculture.*

9. Clifton R. Wharton, Jr., "Research on Agricultural Development in Southeast Asia," *Journal of Farm Economics Proceedings,* 45 (December 1963), 1161–74. In the literature cited by Wharton item 31 merits special attention, namely "Education and Agricultural Growth" by Wharton. Also see, "Investing in Farm People," Chapter 12 of *Transforming Traditional Agriculture.*

10. Anthony M. Tang, "Research and Education in Japanese Agricultural Development, 1880–1938," *The Economic Studies Quarterly,* XIII (1963), Table 2 and p. 97.

CHAPTER IV

1. From an index of 81 to 112 between 1945 and 1963. See *Economic Report of the President*, 1964, Table C-73.
2. Based on cropland harvested in these states in 1959. *Statistical Abstract of the United States, 1962*, Table 860, p. 625.
3. During the period from 1945–46 to 1960–61.
4. Tara Shukla, "Capital Formation in Agriculture in India, 1920–21 to 1960–61" (unpublished Ph.D. dissertation, Department of Economics, University of Bombay, 1963).
5. From 1945 to 1963. The figures for 1963 are preliminary estimates.
6. Vernon W. Ruttan, "Technological Changes and Resources Utilization in American Agriculture," *Proceedings of the Indiana Academy of Science for 1961*, 71 (1961), 353–60.
7. See "Factors of Production Concealed under 'Technological Change,'" Chapter 9 of my *Transforming Traditional Agriculture*.
8. Raymond P. Christensen, William E. Hendrix, and Robert D. Stevens, *How the United States Improved Its Agriculture*, Econ. Res. Service, U.S.D.A., Foreign —76. Table 6 shows the ratio of prices received for crops to the prices of fertilizer as follows:

Period	Ratio
1935–39	1.00
1950–52	1.75
1957–59	1.51

9. Zvi Griliches, "Research Costs and Social Returns: Hybrid Corn and Related Innovations," *The Journal of Political Economy*, 66 (October 1958).

10. Zvi Griliches, "The Sources of Measured Productivity Growth: United States Agriculture, 1940–1960," *The Journal of Political Economy,* 71 (August 1963). See also his "Research Expenditures, Education, and the Aggregate Agricultural Production Function," *American Economic Review,* December 1964.

11. D. Gale Johnson's recent paper, "Soviet Agriculture," *Bulletin of Atomic Scientists,* January 1964, is an excellent review of the effects of governmental policy and programs.

12. Gregor Lazarcik, "Factors Affecting Production and Productivity in Czechoslovak Agriculture, 1934–38 and 1946–60," *Journal of Farm Economics,* 45 (February 1963), 205–18.

13. *Ibid.,* Table 3, p. 214.

14. The treatment that follows is based on my paper, "A Policy to Redistribute Losses from Economic Progress," *Journal of Farm Economics,* 43 (August 1961). This paper also appears as an essay in *Labor Mobility and Population in Agriculture* (Ames: Iowa State University Press, ©️ 1961). I am grateful to the *Journal* and to the Press for permission to use parts of this paper here.

15. In the paper already cited, on which I have drawn, I had occasion to outline in some detail the particular measures appropriate to the U.S. agricultural situation.

16. My comments here are based on a paper which I read before the National Farm Institute, Des Moines, Iowa, February 13, 1964. It appeared in *The Social Service Review* (University of Chicago Press), 38, No. 2 (June 1964), 123–29. I am grateful to *The Review* and the Press for permission to use parts of it here.

17. See Jacob Viner, "The United States as a 'Welfare State,'" in *Man, Science, Learning and Education,* ed. by Sanford W. Higginbotham (Rice University, 1963), p. 215.

18. The Farm Bureau, led by Ed O'Neal during the New Deal, continued to support these aims. Christiana McFadyen Campbell in her excellent study *The Farm Bureau and the New Deal* (Urbana: University of Illinois Press, 1962), p. 48, notes: "The old agrarian stand-bys of trust-busting and currency reform . . . were still doggedly in the Farm Bureau's resolutions." Also, page 187: "Farm Bureau support for the anti-trust campaign of the Department of Justice (under Thurman Arnold) was not confined to good wishes, but was applied where it counted most—that is, to Congressional appropriations." The rest of her paragraph on this matter is most telling.

19. The high level of economic sophistication with respect to monetary policy of Allan B. Kline, who followed Ed O'Neal as president of the Farm Bureau, was not excelled by any lay leaders either in business or labor of that period.

20. The response came during the first term of the Wilson administration, when a constitutional amendment was finally approved; progressive taxation was then enacted to begin to redress the existing inequalities in personal income and wealth.

21. They did, however, acquire among others, the following: Rural free delivery of the mail—RFD; improved farm roads often better, at least until recently, than the roads in our cities; cooperatives to provide electricity and telephone services to farmers; and some credit to improve farm homes. Land-grant colleges and universities began mainly as an agricultural

venture. They are undoubtedly one of our out-
standing institutional innovations. While they have
contributed to the dignity of farming and to its
modernization and productivity, the economic benefits have become widely diffused among predominantly nonfarm consumers.

22. The extension of old-age and survivor benefits to farm
people explains in large part the *sharp* improvement
in their lot since the middle 1950's. In 1954 the
median incomes of farm families with heads of family
age 65 and over was only 57 percent that of rural
nonfarm families, $1,091 and $1,929, respectively. By
1960 this gap had virtually disappeared; for farm
families, head age 65 and over, it was $2,294 and
that of rural nonfarm, $2,352.

23. It should be noted that the National Farmers Union
has supported these measures.

24. This estimate is based on a value of all farm real
estate of $144 billion of which about 37 percent was
owned by landlords who were not farming (although
some of them lived on farms). Attributing 63 percent to farmers equals $90.7 billion. Add to this live-
stock, machinery, motor vehicles, and crops, and
the total is $136.3 billion. Financial assets amounted
to $18.4 billion; altogether $154.7 billion. Claims
(debts) were as follows: Farm real estate, $15.2
billion, and attributing all of this to farmers (none
to landlords not farming even though they surely
have some of it), the total debt of farmers would
be $30 billion. Then 154.7 − 30.0 = $124.7 billion of
net assets. Divide this by 3,481,000 farmers and one
derives $35,832 net assets owned per farmer. Source:
Economic Report of the President, 1964, Table C-76.

25. I am, of course, aware that the Farm Bureau cur-

rently issues some statements pertaining to governmental social services that read as if they were pure
nineteenth-century laissez faire. But every special
interest group is to some extent a victim of its own
oversimplification of political issues in its attempts
to "sell" its policy approach.

26. William H. Nicholls, *Southern Tradition and Regional Progress* (Chapel Hill: University of North Carolina Press, 1960).

Index

Abdel-Wahab, A. R., 102
Absentee landlords, 28
Acceptance rate, 66, 74, 77
Agricultural colleges, 2, 41-42, 109
American Indians, 91
Animal husbandry, 58
Anthropologists, 6, 23-24
Argentina, 55
Asia, 2, 5, 7, 12, 54, 63, 97, 105
Australia, 8
Austria, 53-54

Bad press, 22, 26
Brazil, 10, 37, 45, 54, 63
Brown, Lester R., 12, 97, 102
Burma, 12, 50

Calories, 9
Cambodia, 12
Campbell, Christiana Mc-Fadyen, 108
Canada, 8
Capital, 3, 5, 11, 16, 18-20, 37-38, 44, 71, 82, 85, 99, 106
Cassava, 102
Ceylon, 50
Chile, 54, 55
China, 1, 19
Cho, Yong Sam, 103
Christensen, Raymond P., 106
Christy, Francis T., Jr., 105
Cocoa beans, 32
Collective farms, 5
Colombia, 54-55
Comparative advantage, 4
Conflict of interest, 92, 95

Congress, 95
Cooperatives, 64, 106
Corn, 31-33, 48, 61, 63, 75, 102, 104; hybrid, 5, 19-20, 32, 66, 73-74, 76, 106
Costa Rica, 56
Cotton, 32-33, 103
Credit, 17, 42, 49, 57-58, 82
Cultural, 21-22, 24-25, 31, 39, 86
Czechoslovakia, 76, 107

Demand, 8, 10, 66, 79
Demonstration, 67
Depressed areas, 80, 84
Disequilibrium, 14-16, 44
Disguised unemployment, 13, 29
Dominican Republic, 56

Economic efficiency, 6, 8, 15, 45
Economic equilibrium, 14-16, 20, 36, 44
Economic growth, 9, 15, 20, 23-25, 36, 39, 40, 44-45, 56-58, 65
Economic opportunities, 14, 35, 39, 57
Economic stability, 84, 86, 87
Econometric studies, 32
Engel's law, 10, 98
Erosion control, 91
Expectations, 42-43
Extension activities, 5, 35, 41-42, 46-47, 49, 52, 57-59, 65-68, 74

Falcon, Walter P., 33, 103
Far East, 54

Farm Bureau, 106, 110
Farm management, 58
Farm size, 11-13, 28, 101
Farm tenure, 6
Farm workers, 30
Federal Reserve System, 88
Fertilizer, 29, 32-33, 45-46, 48-51, 73, 75-76, 104, 106
Firms for profit, 52, 59, 65, 67
Fisher, Franklin M., 97
Food, 10, 18-19, 21, 40, 75, 98
Forward prices, 95
France, 24, 48

Gains in productivity, 70, 72, 75-78, 106
Garlock, Fred L., 99
Geertz, Clifford, 100
Ghana, 32
Goreux, L. M., 98
Grange, 91
Grazing, 91
Greece, 53-54
Griliches, Zvi, 74-75, 106-7
Grunwald, Joseph, 102
Guatemala, 34, 38
Gupta, S. C., 102

Hagen, Everett E., 23, 100
Haiti, 19, 56
Hatch Act, 72, 105
Health facilities, 89, 91
Hendrix, William E., 106
Higginbotham, Sanford W., 108
Highway, 37, 45
Hirschman, A. O., 102
Hopper, W. David, 24, 30, 34, 38-39, 101, 103
Houthakker, H. S., 10, 98
Hume, David, 26-27, 100
Hypothesis, 15-17, 20-21, 35-36

Ideology, 41, 47
Incentives, 7, 17, 20, 25, 31, 39, 47, 51, 77, 82-83
Income, 8, 10-11, 14, 27, 59, 88, 90, 94, 98, 104
Income elasticity, 10
India, 3, 5, 9-13, 19-20, 24, 32-35, 37-39, 45, 48-51, 54-55, 62-64, 71-72, 97-103, 105-6
Indolence, 18, 22, 26-27
Indonesia, 12, 100
Industrialization, Preface, 27, 93
Inputs, 5-6, 20, 29-30, 34, 36, 46-47, 58, 60-61, 65, 71-73, 105
Insecticides, 46, 73
Interest, 38
International commodity markets, 2
International Rice Research Institute, 63-64
International trade, 3, 6, 12
International Wheat Agreement, 2
Investment, 11, 17, 20, 27, 30-31, 36-37, 40, 44, 51-52, 59, 68, 71, 81, 96
Irrigation, 16, 37-38, 44-46, 71, 76, 99
Israel, 53-54, 70, 97
Italy, 50

Jacobsen, Thorkild, 99
Japan, 4-5, 8, 12-13, 19-20, 33-35, 45, 48-50, 53-54, 63, 68, 70, 97, 99, 105
Johnson, D. Gale, 101, 107
Jute, 32, 103

Kenaf, 102
Khatkhate, D. R., 101
Krishna, Raj, 32-33, 101, 103

Labor, 5, 16, 19, 71, 83, 89, 99
Labor force, 71, 74, 86
Laissez-faire, 88, 91, 110
Land, 4-5, 11, 16, 19, 27, 30, 38-39, 45, 71, 91, 99
Landed aristocracy, 26, 28
Land-grant universities, Preface, 41, 89, 93
Landowners, 25, 94
Land reform, 42
Latin America, 32, 45, 54-55, 62-63, 102, 105
Law, 6
Lazarcik, Gregor, 107
Learning, 66-67, 77
Lewis, W. Arthur, 27, 100
Losses, 70, 79-83, 85, 87, 106

Machinery, 11, 38, 40, 73, 86
Majid, A., 102
Marx, Karl, 26, 28, 88
McClelland, David C., 100
McNary-Haugenism, 88, 94
Mexican nationals, 91
Mexico, 8, 32, 37, 46, 53-54, 58, 63-64, 70, 97
Migration, 81
Miller Paiva, Ruy, 104
Monetary-fiscal, 84, 88, 93
Morrill Act, 105
Mosher, Martin L., 61, 104

Nair, Kusum, 102
National Farmers' Union, 109
Negroes, 90, 91, 93
Nerlove, Marc L., 32
New Deal, 88, 90, 106
New Zealand, 8
Nicholls, W. H., 28, 92, 101, 104, 110
Non-Partisan League, 91

Old age and survivor insurance, 89, 109

Output, 6, 7, 20, 31, 33, 105

Pakistan, 12, 33, 54-55, 101, 103
Paraguay, 56
Payoff, 15, 37, 40, 46, 60, 62, 64, 75
Permanent income stream, 104
Peru, 19, 54, 56, 65
Perverse farmers, 1-2, 4, 6, 49
Pesticides, 73
Philippines, 12, 53-55, 63-64
Potter, Neal, 105
Preferences, 21-22, 24-25, 43, 52
Point Four programs, 55
Politics, 6, 27, 60, 87
Population, 7, 10, 12, 19, 55, 77, 99
Populists, 91
Prices, 12-13, 19, 25, 32, 34-35, 39, 48-51, 59, 78, 97, 102-3, 106
Production possibilities, 14, 21, 29, 80
Productivity of labor, 71
Profitability, 24, 36, 58, 66, 95
Public Law 480, 3, 7, 51, 97
Punjab, 32-33, 38, 101, 103
Puzzles, 4, 5, 7, 11, 20, 72, 91

Rates of return, 25-26, 31, 36-38, 44, 52, 68, 75
Rent, 27
Research, 5, 41, 46-47, 52-53, 59, 61-64, 68, 73-74, 76, 89, 105
Ricardo, David, 26
Rice, 5, 9, 19, 33, 50
Risk and uncertainty, 36
Rockefeller Foundation, 53, 63
Rosenberg, Nathan, 100

Rotwein, Eugene, 100
Ruttan, Vernon, 72, 105-6

Savings, 17, 20, 24, 30, 38, 57
Savings deposit, 38
Scale effects, 75
Schooling, 5, 25, 28, 46-47, 52, 59, 67-68, 74-75, 90-91, 93, 95-96
Schultz, Theodore W., 97, 99, 101, 103-7
Seed multiplication, 64
Senapur, India, 23, 30, 34, 37-39
Shukla, Tara, 99, 106
Skills, 33, 46, 67, 71, 74, 81, 86
Smith, Adam, 26
Socialism, 88
Sociologists, 23
Soils, 58, 60, 73
Sources of income, 60
South Korea, 103
Southern Tradition, 28, 92, 95, 101, 110
Soviet Union, 2, 5, 19, 27-28, 41, 69-70, 75-77, 101, 107
State of the arts, 30, 39-40, 43, 52, 95-96
Stevens, Robert D., 106
Subsidies, 4, 6, 78
Sudan, 32, 102
Sugar cane, 32, 48, 102, 104
Supply, 8, 19, 33, 60, 62, 65, 73, 79
Supply responses, 32, 101, 103

Taiwan, 5, 12, 53-55
Tang, Anthony M., 68, 105

Tax, Sol, 23-24, 34, 103
Technical assistance, 42, 55-56, 63
Technology, 23, 72, 105-6
Thailand, 12-13, 31, 50-51, 99, 102
Thrift, 18, 25, 59
Tractor, 20, 46, 73, 99
Turkey, 54

Underemployment, 16
Underpricing, 51
Unemployment, 84, 85-86, 89
United Arab Republic, 50
United States, 2-5, 8-11, 19, 33-34, 38, 41-42, 47-48, 50-51, 55-56, 58, 61-65, 67, 70-72, 75, 77-78, 80, 88, 90-94, 97-99, 106-8
University contracts, 42, 64
Uruguay, 55

Venezuela, 56
Venkataramanan, L. S., 32, 103
Viner, Jacob, 87, 108

Wealth, 88, 90, 94
Welfare, 8, 78, 85, 92, 94
Welfare state, 87, 91, 93, 106
West Germany, 2
Western Europe, 2-4, 8, 19, 34, 41, 53-54, 70, 76
Wharton, Clifton R., Jr., 105
Wheat, 9, 32-33, 50
Wilcox, W. W., 10, 98
Windfall gains, 79
Work, 25, 30, 100
Wright, Gordon, 24